D1505535

I AM CANADA

FIRE IN THE SKY

World War I

by David Ward

Scholastic Canada Ltd.
Toronto New York London Auckland Sydney
Mexico City New Delhi Hong Kong Buenos Aires

While the events described and some of the characters in this book
may be based on actual historical events and real people,
Paul Townend is a fictional character created by the author,
and his story is a work of fiction.

A Dear Canada Book. Published by Scholastic Canada Ltd.
SCHOLASTIC and I AM CANADA and logos are trademarks
and/or registered trademarks of Scholastic Inc.

www.scholastic.ca

Library and Archives Canada Cataloguing in Publication

Ward, David, 1967-
Fire in the sky / by David Ward.

Issued also in electronic format.
ISBN 978-1-4431-0400-5

1. Richthofen, Manfred, Freiherr von, 1892-1918--Juvenile fiction.
2. World War, 1914-1918--Aerial operations, Canadian--Juvenile fiction.
I. Title.

PS8595.A69F57 2013   jC813'.6   C2013-901799-2

6 5 4 3 2 1   Printed in Canada 114   13 14 15 16 17

The display type was set in Immortal.
The text was set in Minion.

First printing September 2013

For Tim Rourke — a man of honour

Prologue

I cannot claim to have known the Red Baron or even met him, as some of my friends have boasted. But I have *seen* him pass through the sights of my Lewis .303 machine gun on a blustery day above the fields of France. And I have glimpsed him racing for my tail, his bullets ripping the fabric off my wings. Nothing could have prepared me for such a sight. But then again, no one could have imagined the horrors unleashed on Europe in 1914, when I was just seventeen.

* * *

Robert and I were finishing raking a line of hay when our little sister came racing out to us.

"Daddy says to come," she said, her eyes wide with excitement and worry.

Robert mopped his brow. "Why so worried, Sarah?"

"There will be war," she said at last. "Germany has invaded Belgium and the doctor says England will get involved." Her lip trembled. "The doctor came in a car to see Momma. He said the story is all over the newspapers."

Robert drove his pitchfork deep into the earth, then grabbed me around the shoulders. He swung me in an arc till my feet caught and we tumbled to the ground. I flung a fistful of hay and caught his open mouth. He tackled me and, as always, I ended up on my back.

"You hear that, little brother?" he shouted. Straw slipped from his curly hair. "Some excitement at last!"

The endless prairie sky suddenly called out the infinite possibilities of faraway lands and adventure instead of hay and heat and toil — farm work that went on forever.

When we were little, Robert once told me that the sky ended at the horizon somewhere beyond Winnipeg. "One day," he said, "we'll get on the train and step out of the bubble. We'll see what it's like outside!" That day had come with the announcement of war.

But Sarah shouted, "Stop it! Stop it!" Tears ran down her cheeks. "You'll both be gone away."

"We won't leave you so easily," I assured her.

"Paul can't leave anyway," Robert said. "He's only seventeen. But I promise to write you both!"

We chased him all the way to the house.

My father waited on the porch steps. With one hand he held his wide-brimmed hat and the

2

other he ran through his hair. From a distance he looked just like Robert, his tall frame leaning against a porch post. He flashed a brief smile as we approached, but his mood was serious. My mother sat motionless on the porch swing.

"It's true?" Robert asked. "War?"

Father nodded. "So they say. Canada will follow Britain."

"I want to enlist," Robert said.

On the way to the house my thoughts had been spinning with so many questions. Now, in front of my father, it was obvious what the conversation was going to be about.

He cleared his throat. "Your mother and I thought that might be the way of it. I won't try to change your mind, son. It is your right. But I was hoping you might stay with us till Christmas."

Looking beyond my father, Robert said to my mother, "It might be over by Christmas!"

"No one knows that," she said quietly.

There was a long silence. My excitement drained away and I felt the first pangs of worry.

"Well," Father said presently. "There's a lot of hay to get in the barn before anyone can enlist. Might as well get to it. Won't help the cows any if we dawdle."

My brother enlisted in the second week of

September and joined one of Winnipeg's regiments in the Canadian Expeditionary Force. It was the loneliest moment of my life. I spent the next two years thinking of how I would join him.

We had not been apart from the day I was born. Although he was two years my senior, I was the steady one, the planner. I made sure we didn't get into trouble. And who would do that if I was not with him?

No one was surprised that Robert joined the army. He was impulsive — a man of action, my father said. I remembered many of Robert's quick decisions. I glanced at a sketch I had made and tacked to the wall. It was the day the mayor's deputy crashed his car on our farm and ignited the gas in the can he'd fastened to the running board.

In the picture I stood frozen, staring at the smoke and the flames. Robert was climbing through the window to rescue the driver. The picture was not exactly what happened, but it was what I'd felt like: frozen in the face of danger.

I closed my eyes and remembered. It was the first time I'd seen a car, and it was frightening to watch the flames creep over it.

"Paul!" Robert had shouted. He shook me. "We've got to get him out!" He shook me again and I came out of my shock.

"Try the door!" I said. Robert ran right up to the car with his face half covered by his shirt to protect him against the smoke.

"It's stuck!" he choked out.

I stumbled into the ditch. Inside, the driver had slumped far over to the passenger's side.

"Punch out the window," I shouted. Robert's fist shattered the glass. Blood smeared the paint as he brushed against the doorframe. "Lift me higher!" he commanded. He heaved himself up on the window. I caught his legs and hoisted him into the car. There was a loud grunt, and then Robert was dragging the unconscious man out. "Hurry!" I shouted.

Flames leapt around the cab as we hauled him to the top of the bank.

The deputy survived, and Robert and I were declared heroes. But I knew there was only one hero: my brother.

As always, I drew just about everything that happened. When Robert saw my sketch, he touched the picture and then said something that changed me: "Always move towards the fear. Even if your knees shake. Just walk towards it. Half the time the fear will run the other way. The other half . . . well, take it as it comes." He ruffled my hair. "You're smart, Paul, but sometimes you think too much."

Chapter 1
August 1916

The war did not end at Christmas. Robert's letters indicated that he had finally seen action and, based on the newspapers, we guessed that his division had been at Ypres in April of 1915, where the enemy first used chlorine gas. Mother and Father were greatly worried until his next letter arrived to say that all was well.

His letters home, spotty though they were — and many of them censored — spoke of some of the same hideous details we got from the radio or the newspapers. His words about the agony of the soldiers who were gassed by the Germans, and the horror of learning that the *Lusitania* had been sunk by a U-boat in May of 1915, were difficult to read. My hands shook when I read about the devastating bombardments at Mount Sorrel in June of 1916. But the setbacks only seemed to spur Robert on.

Time went by agonizingly slowly on the farm while Robert remained determined to do his bit and help England win the war. Father had asked that I stay through the haying season when I turned eighteen, and without Robert around, I had honoured his request, even though the determination in Robert's letters was contagious. Mother nervously watched me as my nineteenth birthday approached. But it was something far different from anything my parents could have guessed that made me decide how I would join Robert in the war. And it happened in the same month as my birthday.

Father and I were loading haystacks into the wagon on a blistering August day. Suddenly something burst into view and split the silence of the summer. It was in the sky and coming low over the trees. I did not know what it was until it was within 50 feet of us. It was an airplane, a sleek-winged wonder that roared above our heads. From the stunned look on my father's face, I knew he was just as surprised as I was. Like a knight fighting a dragon, he raised his pitchfork to ward off the monster.

But the airplane was no monster to me. It was as graceful as a bird. The pilot dipped his wings and waved. I waved back. From that moment I knew what part I wanted to play in The Great War.

Another year went by and, much to my mother's dismay, on my nineteenth birthday, in August,

1916, I decided to leave for Ontario to join the Royal Naval Air Service. My timing wasn't the best: only one month earlier, almost a whole regiment from Newfoundland had been lost in just one battle. My father shook my hand and told me he was proud. "Say your prayers every night, son," he said. "We'll do the same for you here."

Leaving the farm was one of the most difficult decisions I have ever made. And Robert was not there to shake me from my indecision.

Sarah didn't help either. She cried and held on to me at the train station. I gave her a bear hug and promised to write her often. "You won't," she accused me through her tears.

I tweaked her nose. "Didn't I just say that I would? And I'll draw you pictures of flying machines and of France!" In the end I stepped on to the train and for the first time stepped out of the bubble and into the world beyond our town.

The Royal Naval Air Service immediately sent a group of us to the Curtiss Aviation School in Toronto for flight training. The train ride was long and there seemed no end of fields and forests. As we approached the Great Lakes I was stunned at how big they were and wondered if the ocean might look the same.

On the train I met Billy Miller and we struck

up a friendship immediately. Although only a year older than me, he already had a full moustache. He winked at me when I said I was unable to grow either a beard or a moustache. Then he gave the ends a twirl and said, "Hurrah!" It was a phrase that stuck and he used it quite frequently from then on.

When I asked him why he chose the RNAS, Billy said, "I lost a brother in the trenches. Didn't seem like a decent way to die. Besides, I saw a flying machine at the Winnipeg Industrial Exhibition in 1914 and it struck me that the pilot was a man in control of his own destiny. That's how I want to fight. Not caught like a rat in a stinking trench."

Billy told me that we ought to consider ourselves lucky. The lads that had come to the flying school a few months earlier had had to pay their own tuition and as much as four hundred dollars! He also said that hundreds of them had been turned down and had to join the regular army. There simply weren't enough planes or experienced pilots to train the large numbers of men enlisting.

There was much excitement when the wood and canvas buildings that housed the planes of the Curtiss Aviation School came into view. Our enthusiasm did not lessen, not even when we saw that our huts were small and contained only beds and a stove. I didn't care. My attention was held by something on the dirt field that stretched out for a half mile beyond the huts.

There, in all its glory, was a flying machine, touching down in a cloud of dust and showing off for our arrival. Two men in overalls hurried out from the hangar and ran alongside the plane, holding onto the tail.

The plane bumped along the field and came to a stop not far from the first huts. It had two sets of wings — a biplane — and was so much sleeker than the plane my father and I had witnessed above our farm. I recognized the shape. It had two cockpits, one for the pilot and one for the trainee. I felt a rush of excitement that this might be the plane used for our own training.

The moment the train stopped, Billy and I grabbed our bags and raced onto the field towards the plane. "What a beauty!" Billy shouted.

The pilot stepped down, raised his goggles and removed his leather flying gloves. Then he stretched his legs and arms.

"Hello, boys," he greeted us. I wasn't surprised by his American accent. We had been told that most of our training pilots were American and so were our planes. On the train, I'd read everything they gave me at the recruiting office, and had already begun to sketch the planes from the briefing papers.

"She's gorgeous," Billy said, running his hand over the canvas of the wing.

"She's a Curtiss Jenny," I said quietly. "A JN-3."

"Hur*rah*," said Billy, and he twirled his moustache at me.

The pilot nodded and slapped me on the shoulder. "What's your name?"

"Paul Townend, sir."

"Well, Paul Townend. My name is Fred Martin. It seems you've got a jump on your mates here. I think you'll be the first one in the air with me. I've never had a student who could name the Jenny on first sight."

I looked up eagerly. "Right now, sir?"

He laughed. "I've just flown from New York State, my boy. My feet are numb and I need coffee." He nodded towards the plane. "This is your trainer. We'll start in the morning, all right?"

Mr. Martin stamped some life back into his feet and then headed for one of the huts. Billy gave me a shove and called me a show-off. I crashed into two others and a wrestling match broke out. I ended up on the bottom of the pile, laughing. Mr. Martin stopped and watched us from a distance.

I could not eat supper that night. All I could

think about was flying the Curtiss Jenny in the morning. "Here's to wee Paul," Billy said as he raised his glass. "The first flyer among us."

In my bunk that night, after I'd said my prayers, I whispered down to Billy, "Did you see the way Fred pushed his goggles up so smartly and tucked his gloves under his arm? A real pilot!"

"Shut up, Paul," was the only reply.

Chapter 2
August 1916

Mr. Martin met us early, on the field. There was no bugle, as the Curtiss Aviation School was privately owned and not an army institution. It was strange to be in our uniforms when there were no officers in charge. Even Fred Martin was not military and we called him "Mr. Martin," not "sir. "

Mr. Martin stood with his arms folded and stared out at the rising sun. His gloves were tucked under his arm. A waft of cigarette smoke met us as we approached.

"Good morning, boys!" He tossed his cigarette to the ground. "Hardly a breath of wind; sun's up. You're in for a good ride, Mr. Townend."

I straightened my uniform and tried to stop my hands from shaking. "I'm ready, Mr. Martin."

He looked me up and down. "Not in that, you're not," he said. "We're going up six thousand five hundred feet, son. It's a tad colder at that altitude. And there will be wind." He pointed to a set of benches against the nearest hut. We walked over and Mr. Martin began our first lesson.

"I am not a fighting pilot, lads," he said. "But I can tell you that unless you are prepared for the skies, you will be useless for your cause. Whether you're operating a camera to see what the Germans are up to, or chasing an enemy plane, you can't afford frozen hands." He raised an eyebrow at me. "You would not want frozen fingers when it comes time to squeeze the trigger, would you, Mr. Townend?"

"No, Mr. Martin," I replied.

He gripped Billy's shoulder. "And what would you do if your friend Paul here has an Albatros on his tail and your eyes are covered in castor oil spray from the rotary engines they use over in France?"

Billy winked at me. "Isn't it bad luck to shoot an albatross, Mr. Martin?"

Mr. Martin did not laugh. "*Albatros*, as the Germans say," he replied. "And you will need all the luck you've got, son. Because that particular bird carries synchronized machine guns and fires continuously until your plane is full of holes."

There was a long silence. Mr. Martin pointed to the bench again. "Now, you'll need a helmet, gloves and a coat. In the winter you will wear a good deal more and it still won't be enough. If you're lucky," and he gave Billy a stare, "they'll have battery-

14

operated heaters in the jackets over in France."

Someone muttered something about electric underwear but the laughter was quelled by a glare from Mr. Martin.

I hurriedly buttoned on the leather coat and tightened the belt around my waist. There was a large pocket stitched diagonally across the chest. I eyed it with interest.

"That's for your maps. It's very easy to get lost in the air," Mr. Martin said. "Especially at night. A flyer must pay attention to landmarks. Things look different from the heights."

The gloves were enormous and clumsy and came up to my elbows. They didn't look as sleek and fancy as our instructor's and were clearly for keeping the passenger warm. "You'll be thankful for those soon enough," Mr. Martin said.

Finally, I put on the helmet and goggles. The helmet was more like a cap with flaps that came down over my ears. Billy fastened my chinstrap. He was serious now but he still clapped my shoulder and gave me a grin. I walked stiffly to the plane, my heart racing. All the gear I had on left me feeling a good deal warmer.

Mr. Martin indicated a step strategically indented into the body of the plane between the two flier seats. "Up you go, Mr. Townend."

I placed my foot and stepped onto the lower wing, making for the cockpit closest to the rear.

"No, no," Mr. Martin said to me. "The pilot sits aft. The trainee sits fore. At least for the first time. After a few hours of instruction in the days ahead, you'll sit in my seat." I swung my leg up and climbed clumsily into the front seat. A control stick protruded from the floor, and seven or eight gauges with numbers and needles stared back at me. I looked at them helplessly and wondered suddenly if Mr. Martin actually intended for me to fly the plane.

Mr. Martin read my mind. "Do not touch anything, Mr. Townend," he said. "I have the same controls. This is a free ride for your sharp answer of yesterday! Indeed, it may be the only ride you have in a Jenny for some time."

I glanced down at my fellow trainees as I struggled with the safety belt a bit and then managed to strap myself in. They grinned and waved at me. Mr. Martin stood in his cockpit, looking at my shoulder. "Good. You've figured that out. Make sure it's tight. You'll have need of it."

From my peripheral vision I saw a man in overalls, presumably a mechanic, walk to the front of the plane. He gave Mr. Martin a wave and stood in front of the propeller. I had some trouble seeing what he was doing. A few of the lads ran around to see what he was up to, but he waved them away and pointed to the rear of the plane. Billy and another lad ran back and each gripped a flap on the tail.

"Pay close attention, Mr. Townend," Mr. Martin said. "This step is critical and you are receiving a rare opportunity. There are usually hours of book work before you get to this stage."

I nodded and tuned out everything other than the mechanic and Mr. Martin. What happened next was a series of exchanges between the two men that sounded like a code.

"Petrol on!" the mechanic yelled. Then he said, "Switch off!"

"Switch off!" Mr. Martin repeated.

I heard a clicking sound.

"Suck in!" the mechanic yelled. I saw him reach up and grip the propeller blade. He turned it in a wide arc, once around, and then again. I could feel the motion and tug on the front of the plane.

"Contact!" the mechanic called.

"Contact!" Mr. Martin said.

The mechanic gave the propeller a hard swing, followed by another, and another. Suddenly the prop turned fully around on its own. The engine coughed. The prop continued to turn, slowly at first, caught once, and then turned faster and faster, with the engine coughing and sputtering. Then the engine roared to life and the propeller turned with such speed I could no longer follow its rotations. Wind blasted in my face and the plane became a living thing, pulling and tugging on its wheel blocks as if it wanted to leap into the skies.

Mr. Martin shouted something but I couldn't hear a thing above the roaring engine. Every piece of metal and wood around me seemed to shake and vibrate. Mr. Martin patted my shoulder and then gave me a thumbs-up. I reached back so he could see my own thumb in return. It was the moment I'd been waiting for ever since my first glimpse of a plane.

The mechanic scurried over to the inside of the wing and reached down towards the wheels. He pulled the wheel block away and I caught sight of a student doing the same on the other side. The Jenny began to move!

The flaps on the top wing suddenly lifted. Then the lower wing flaps also rose. I realized Mr. Martin was testing to make certain that all was in working order. A moment later I heard an increase in throttle. The wires and wooden struts on the wings rattled along with the noise of the engine. I shouted happily and raised my fists in the air.

Once again Mr. Martin increased throttle. The wind blew more strongly against my face, and when I glanced to the side, I realized with a shock that Billy and the lads were some 50 yards behind us. With every second I felt a growing pressure on my chest, as if unseen hands were pushing me back. We bumped along as the Jenny picked up speed. My head and shoulders lurched and shifted constantly. It felt something like riding my bicycle after a heavy rain, when the gravel on the road was filled with dips. My arms would shake and there would be a jarring bump when I could not avoid a pothole. Only this was so much faster and the wind terrifically strong.

I felt a larger bump beneath us and looked out. The Jenny leapt into the air!

I could suddenly feel the weight of the plane as we pressed against the air, rising higher and higher. The sensation was so exhilarating I found myself shouting for joy and holding my arms out like wings. Far below, the aerodrome's school buildings looked like painted wooden blocks on a green field. Something moved along the ground and I saw a train, just like the one that had brought us to Toronto, making its way through a copse of trees. Its steam broke above the green in billowing clouds. Farmers' fences criss-crossed the fields to the horizon, and dotted here and there were tiny specks making their way through the pastures.

How Sarah would have loved to see what I was seeing!

We slowed and the vibration of the struts and wires lessened. The next thing I knew, we were banking to the left and the world opened up beneath me as the wings dipped. I was so close to the air and sky that if I had not been strapped in I would have spilled out and joined the clouds. Far from being frightened, I had the greatest feeling of my life. Although I knew Mr. Martin couldn't hear me, I shouted, "Do it again!"

He straightened out the Jenny and we flew smoothly for a minute or so. Then he banked left again and I spotted the aerodrome up ahead, with its signature white roofs and dirt field. I pointed at it. Mr. Martin reached forward and gave a thumbs-up signal. We flew right past it and I breathed a sigh of relief. I'd thought he was going to end the ride and land. Instead he began to dive.

At first I thought he was simply bringing us down to level off. But when he didn't stop and the nose continued to point downward, I knew something else was about to happen. The engine roared and the wings rattled violently. Suddenly we began to rise up again, sharply. We continued until all I could see anywhere was the sky. My stomach dropped. The next instant we were upside down, with the earth spinning below and the weight of a cow pressed against my chest. All the blood rushed to my head.

I had read that pilots were able to complete loops, and that the manoeuvre was part of training. But *experiencing* a loop taught me instantly that reading about something and doing the real thing were two different realities. I clutched my stomach to keep it from falling out of my mouth.

I managed to keep my eyes open and saw the horizon, a massive tilted line, through the Jenny's wings. The plane looped round and the sky came back to where it belonged and the pressure eased off. I glanced back at Mr. Martin, just to make sure he was still there, and found him laughing like mad. He took his hands from the control stick and clapped. Then he mouthed the word, "Bravo."

Far too soon for my liking, Mr. Martin nosed the Jenny down for a landing. The ground approached quickly as we came closer and closer to the field. Once again my stomach tightened, and I gasped when we made our first contact. Dust spurted like smoke from a fire. We bounced up into the air again and then thumped back down, the giant flaps on the wings working hard to slow our speed. We bumped along the field towards the hangar.

Billy and two others ran alongside us, waving their caps and shouting. Under the instruction of one of the field crew, they took hold of the tail as we slowed down. Soon, blocks were placed beneath the wheels and the Jenny came to rest.

The fellows hoisted me onto their shoulders and marched me around like a hero. When they finally set me down, Mr. Martin strolled up and looked me over. "You did well, Mr. Townend. The last student to complete a loop spilled the contents of his breakfast all over the instrument panel. It took us two days to remove it from the crevices." As he walked away he said over his shoulder, "You're welcome, Mr. Townend."

"Thank you, Mr. Martin, sir!" I shouted.

He gave me his first and only salute.

That night I wrote down the flight from beginning to end in a letter to Sarah: *I may have left the bubble of Winnipeg, little sister, but I could never have dreamed how big the world really is from the sky.*

I sketched the Curtiss Jenny with Billy holding the tail and me giving Sarah a wave from the cockpit. I tried to show the loop by sketching the Jenny in four different positions around a circle. I drew two hands sticking out of the cockpit in triumph at the completion of the loop. Sarah would laugh at that part.

Writing to her caused me to think of Robert. It had been weeks since I'd received a letter from him. Of course, one might have arrived at the farm after I left, and Mother might have sent it on, but it just hadn't arrived yet. I thought of Billy's brother, dead in the trenches, and it turned my stomach more than the loop had done. I prayed right then that God might keep Robert from being killed.

Usually, I would be sitting on the rake behind the horses at this time of year, forming row after row of hay. It was a job that never seemed to end, while heat beat down from a cloudless sky. With me gone, my dad had hired a boy from the church to drive the team. Sarah had taken my job on the rake. They would be all right, I told myself. It was a small farm, only 500 acres, and Dad could always call on a neighbour to help if rain was coming and he had to hurry to get the hay in. I felt no real pangs of homesickness yet. All I knew was that my ride in the Jenny had confirmed my decision to fly.

Chapter 3
August–September 1916

Mr. Martin was right: there was little flying for us in the first few weeks. Tension was high as we watched students from other huts go up in the Jenny day after day. I did manage to go up once more in the next week — me and three others, Billy included, for nearly an hour. I memorized the controls and my instruction manual. We spent the majority of our time learning about the construction and mechanics of planes. The Jenny, I learned, was an amazing flying machine. She weighed over 2000 pounds, a fact that surprised me, since she seemed so light when she was aloft. In the air she rode the wind like a bird and yet, on takeoff or loops, her whole weight pressed down on the pilot. Her top wingspan was 43½ feet. The wings, made of stretched canvas over a wood frame, required a good deal of caution.

In the fourth week of training, we also learned to stitch the canvas. When I asked why, one of the sail makers said, "Do you want to understand your plane or not?"

"No. I just want to shoot down some Germans," Billy muttered.

"Then you're stupid," replied the sail maker. "An expert horseman knows his animal well. He knows what his animal eats and when to apply a blanket or a poultice. A flyer must know his plane. If you don't, I doubt you'll last long."

After flying with Mr. Martin on that first day, I found myself agreeing with the sail maker. I made it my goal to learn everything I possibly could. After my second flight, I made it a habit to sit in a chair in our hut every day, imagining I was in the cockpit. I pressed my feet down as if moving the rudder and moved a broom handle with my hand as a control stick.

"Shall I make some propeller noises for you?" quipped Billy one day as I practised. I decided to humour him and took my makeshift plane into a steep bank. Billy's engine whined as we went into the turn. The door of our hut suddenly opened and one of the lads stood staring at us. Billy and I froze in mid-motion. The man cleared his throat and then said, "When you manage to land, do join us for the soccer match outside."

At the end of August, two events occurred that changed everything for us, and paved the way for Billy and me to go to England. One cloudy morning another Curtiss Jenny arrived. We now had two planes and the prospect of getting some actual flying time. The second event was the graduation of the entire Hut C, who had been given the only share of flying in the Jenny for the past week. With them off to England, Mr. Martin and the new pilot, Mr. Edwards, turned their attention to us.

Late in September I flew again, this time with Mr. Edwards and in the new plane, the JN-4. The Jenny 4 — or Canuck, as our American pilots liked to call her — was faster and stronger than the Jenny 3, with a cruising speed of 60 miles per hour and top speed of 75. The Jenny 4 could also go as high as 11,000 feet. It had a more powerful engine and a higher ceiling capability.

I thought for a moment and then asked, "Can the Germans go higher, Mr. Edwards? It seems to me that if you can be higher than your enemy, you have an advantage."

He gave me a solemn stare. "Yes they can, son — for now. Everyone is working on the problem." He paused and looked at the Jenny. "Mr. Martin tells me you've been up twice and learned quite a bit!"

I nodded.

"Good. Then you'll do a little flying yourself

today. You'll sit aft, and you'll note I've given you flyer's gloves."

I couldn't respond. I just stared at the smart-looking leather gloves.

Then he said, "You will watch for my signal," and he raised his left hand above his shoulder. "Then you take the control stick and rudder."

I was so excited I wanted to yell. So I did. Mr. Edwards smiled and clapped me on the shoulder.

The thrill of taking off from the ground was no less exhilarating than my first time. Whether Mr. Edwards was a better pilot than Mr. Martin or whether the ground had been more fully groomed that day, I couldn't tell, but there were far fewer bumps. We rose steadily and a glance at the altimeter told me we had reached 8000 feet. Mr. Edwards steadied us off and then raised his left hand.

I put my feet into the pedal stirrups on the foot bar experimentally, and immediately felt the tug and sway of the plane. When I took the control stick for the first time, my heart leapt. Being an observer was one thing. Controlling the Jenny was completely different. I felt her every move. Every time the wind buffeted us, I had to balance the pressure I put on the rudder with my feet. I could feel the pull of the propeller and engine on the control stick.

I kept us steady for the first minute, getting used to the tug of the wind and the force I needed to raise or lower the nose. As I prepared for my first turn, I thought back to something the sail maker had said: "An expert horseman knows his animal well." He was right. Flying did feel a little like horseback riding on the farm. The horses liked me at home. I could only hope the Jenny would too.

I took a deep breath and then eased the control stick to port. The Jenny responded beautifully, banking smoothly into the turn. Suddenly the rudder bar pressed against my foot and the Jenny shuddered. I wondered if Mr. Edwards had taken over. Then I remembered something I'd read in my manual. In a turn, the pilot often had to compensate for what was called *adverse yaw,* a drag force caused by the wings that pushed in the opposite direction of the turn.

I applied the rudder firmly and the Jenny eased back into the turn. We banked and straightened out, heading directly over the aerodrome. I glanced ahead to find Mr. Edwards with both of his thumbs up. We tried several more turns in either direction before he took over and we headed back.

"Well done, Mr. Townend," he said when we

landed. "I expect you'll want to do a little more next time."

"I'd like to go up again right now," I answered.

He nodded. "Good lad. You have a natural feel for aircraft."

The next two days I flew with both Mr. Martin and Mr. Edwards, exploring the Jenny's speed and turning capabilities. At one point I had the plane going at full throttle — over 70 miles an hour!

"We're going to try something special today," said Mr. Martin one morning. "You remember our first outing?"

I grinned and nodded.

"Do you think you're up for executing a loop?"

My smile disappeared. "I am, Mr. Martin," I said.

He traced a loop in the air with his finger. "It's a very significant manoeuvre and, once mastered, allows you to attack and defend more effectively."

I took the plane up to 8000 feet, making my turns sharper and sharper in preparation for the more difficult manoeuvre. Finally I signalled to Mr. Martin that I was ready.

I had read about the loop many times, and had pored over an amazing chart that provided step-by-step instructions. I relaxed my shoulders and flexed my fingers.

"Here we go," I murmured. I pushed the control stick forward and began to dive. To complete the loop I needed speed, and a dive was the easiest way to get it. I increased throttle as well and balanced the rudder at my feet. The earth came into view ahead of me. I had increased speed quickly before, but never this steeply.

The wind whistled through the struts and wires and I knew the Jenny was working hard. I pulled back on the stick and the pressure forced me back against my seat. As we hurtled straight upward the engine suddenly sputtered. It sputtered again and then stalled altogether. What a ghastly feeling to be without an engine so high in the sky!

The next thing I knew, Mr. Martin had taken over the controls and we were rolling over and headed back down. The engine caught and roared back into life.

I slapped my knee in frustration. I had ruined it! Mr. Martin looked back at me and tapped his ear. *Listen*, he was saying. *Listen to the engine*. He smiled and moved his finger in an arc. *Do it again.*

I brought us back up to 8000 feet. I realized I had brought the nose up too sharply on the first try, and without enough speed. The manoeuvre needed to be smoother, more natural. The Jenny needed help to complete a loop and I wasn't working with her.

This time I held on to the dive a little longer and gained terrific speed to make the loop. And when I pulled back on the stick to bring us up, I kept the pressure steady, adjusting for the buffeting wind.

The engine laboured again, as it had the last time, and I fought back the urge to even out. I listened more carefully, timing the sound of the engine with the entrance into the loop. We were in the upper arc of the loop now, with the nose high. The engine sputtered but held steady. We had just enough speed to complete the arc!

For a brief moment we were upside down. The blood rushed to my head and I struggled to keep calm. "Almost there," I said to myself. I started humming a Christmas carol and found it easier to focus on the controls. Before I had finished the first verse, the loop was completed. We came back up with the engine roaring and I levelled out.

Mr. Martin gave me a thumbs-up, then took over the controls again and landed in front of a group of students. Despite my numbed fingers and toes, I jumped out of the plane.

"A loop, Billy!" I shouted. "Did you see it?"

He shook my hand. "Well done, Paulie. You

were brilliant." He gave my shoulder a punch. "Now it's my turn."

Billy did extremely well too. He was aggressive in the air, pushing his plane more than I did, taking the turns more steeply and faster. Our two trainers recognized his ability. He had more trouble with the loop than I did, though, and it took him five tries before he could do it without stalling. I came to realize later that stalling happened to the best of pilots and that conditions in war were often nothing as glorious as those we had at Curtiss. In fact, bringing the plane to the point of stalling happened frequently in air battles.

Over the next few days it became clear that Billy and I were getting more hours in the air than the other students. At first I wondered if there was some kind of favouritism going on. I couldn't think why. But the reason soon became clear. In the last days of September Mr. Martin called Billy and me into his hut. He looked serious.

"Well, boys. It appears as if you will be leaving us." He raised a letter he held in his hand. "You two have shown good talent for flying. And they are short of pilots at the Front. They need everyone they can get."

I cleared my throat. "We haven't learned how to

land yet, Mr. Martin. I've only had fifteen hours in the air."

He nodded. "That's three hours more than some of the boys in France. You will learn to land tomorrow if the weather stays clear. We'll start early. Tomorrow night you'll pack your bags and catch the train to New York." He lifted another sheet of paper from the table. "I'm also going to certify you both as pilots once you've completed your landings."

Billy let out a whoop and raised his hands.

"Gentlemen," Mr. Martin added, "you should know that you are filling in vacancies from our former Hut C."

Billy slowly lowered his arms.

"Two men were killed on the first day of training. The planes you'll be using in France are not Jenny 3s or even Jenny 4s and some of them are difficult to fly. In fact, the Royal Flying Corps in Britain is coming up with so many new designs that I'm not keeping up with the latest craft myself. Two of our boys flipped on takeoff."

* * *

That evening, Billy and I took our chairs and sat out on the field in the gathering dusk. Our exuberance was muted after the news of the flyers' deaths. A giant cloud, tinged with red and barely visible, stretched across the sky. Every time I looked up to the heavens these days, I could hardly wait to be back up there. And yet, on that evening, the war seemed much closer, more ominous than glorious. I felt tired and could not stop thinking of Robert. I still had had no word from him.

Finally, in order to shake off the mood, I asked, "Why New York?"

"The ocean," Billy said simply. "We've got to take a ship to England. New York's where the RNAS is shipping out some of their pilots."

I smiled. "So many miles by train and ship, all so that we can fly!"

He grunted. "Indeed!" Then he grew serious. "Paul?"

I gave him my attention.

"My brother said in his letters that lads were often split up when they got to France. Some are sent here, some there. Battalions too, based on the need. It might be like that for us as well. Listen, let's make an agreement to stick together. Let's fight for it and see if we can prove our worth as a team."

I shook his hand. "I'm with you, Billy," I said solemnly.

"Hurrah," he said very quietly. He did not twirl his moustache.

* * *

34

The next morning was cold with a light drizzle of rain. Mr. Martin raised his cigarette and stared at the smoking end, then glanced at the clouds. "Good enough!" he suddenly shouted. "If I can smoke in it, then we can fly in it."

We brought both Jennys out from the hangar and I was paired with Mr. Martin. "Touch down," he said as we climbed in. "Then pull up again. You need to feel the distance between your wheels and the ground."

Soon we were up in the sky and I took over control of the plane. We flew low over the aerodrome for several passes. Then Mr. Martin signalled for me to take the plane down.

I had never flown so low to the ground before on my own and I clenched my teeth as the ground drew closer. We slammed down hard and I pulled up quickly to gain control. Mr. Martin moved his hand slowly through the air to signal me: *Take it easy. Calm down.*

The next attempt was even worse because I was concentrating so much on the control stick that I forgot to adjust my ailerons to make the plane turn. It was also the first time I had flown with another plane so close to me. The first time Billy shot past me I thought we were going to crash. Discerning the distance between planes took some experience.

On my third and fourth attempts at landing, I touched the wheels down more softly and stayed down for several seconds before pulling up. I smirked. It was a little like teasing the ground, or playing tag with the earth. In this game, however, the consequences could be deadly. My final landing was a little rough, but I held the Jenny fairly steady, considering the wind and rain.

When Billy landed a few minutes later, Mr. Martin marched us into his hut. Though we were still in our training coveralls, he pulled off his gloves and signed our papers. "You're pilots!" he announced. "From what I hear, the weather is ten times worse in France, so count yourselves lucky to have had training in the rain."

We both shook Mr. Martin's hand and then Mr. Edwards's. They had been excellent instructors. We were lucky indeed.

Chapter 4
October 1916

We arrived in England in early October. The sea voyage and the foul weather made me realize once again that choosing the air service over the regular navy was a wise decision. It was true that there were fewer German U-boats for our sailors to worry about. The Kaiser did not want the Americans to join the war and he was afraid they might if American ships were sunk. But the lack of U-boats did nothing to ease my seasickness.

Billy did not mind the rough seas. He convinced me to walk in the fresh air, which helped a little. I told him that I preferred doing the loop three times in a row to spending a single hour on a ship. I perked up a little at the sight of Southampton, England.

I had never seen so many people in my life. The streets outside the port were teeming with families and sailors and soldiers. As we made our way through a wicket gate, there was another line of soldiers coming into the port to reach the wharf side. All along the queue, mothers, fathers, sisters, children, wives and girlfriends were saying good-bye to their men. There was a good deal of crying and hugging and kissing going on. It was an odd feeling, travelling in the opposite direction. I wondered who might say goodbye to us when it was our turn to go to France.

I could not help but stare at everything. The seawall surrounding the port was defended by large artillery and anti-aircraft guns. The newly installed armaments stood out impressively against the ancient stone walls. I wondered if the Romans had stood somewhere along this shore long ago and watched the same troubled seas from their towers. There was nothing in Winnipeg, let alone on our farm, that compared with the age and history of England.

And so many people! I heard people speaking in other languages — Italian, perhaps, and definitely French. I knew we would hear French in France, but I had not anticipated hearing it spoken in England.

We passed three men in the line, clearly related, and all receiving their goodbyes from a pretty girl who showered them with hugs and sisterly advice. Billy scooted from our line and stepped in behind the third man. I followed out of habit and wondered what he was up to. When it was Billy's turn, the pretty girl laughed in surprise as he leaned in for a kiss. She gave him a peck on the cheek. Billy moved on and I stood there, embarrassed, not knowing what to do. The girl made sure her brothers were not looking and then motioned me closer. I leaned in to her and she kissed me on the lips! As I made to go she said in my ear, "Good luck, soldier!"

Stupidly, the only thing I could think of saying was, "I'm in the Air Service, Miss." Billy tried to have another turn, but the lads from behind me were already pushing forward and the girl stepped back into the crowd.

"You're the luckiest dog I've ever met," Billy said. "No wonder I decided to keep you around."

"I like England," I responded.

We showed our papers to the officer at the station and asked for the Royal Naval Air Service office. He pointed to a train just coming in. "Take that one," was all he said.

Eventually we ended up at King's Cross Station. London was stunning. There was such a powerful feeling of history and importance hanging about the place. It even smelled old, in a pleasant, exciting sort of way. If I thought the port was busy, then London was insane. There were horses and cabs and cars all moving about, and somehow, miraculously, missing one another.

When we found the RNAS office we received another shock. After glancing at our papers the officer opened a folder on his desk. "Officers Townend and Miller?"

We exchanged glances. "Sir?"

He sighed. "On completion of your flight training you were both promoted. Flight lieutenants, to be precise."

"That's brilliant!" exclaimed Billy.

"Yes, I'm sure," the officer muttered. "Now, for your orders. Tomorrow you are to each ferry a Sopwith Strutter to Redcar, Yorkshire, and report there for further training. We are in great need of planes. Your timing is excellent, gentlemen."

My palms were clammy. I'd never flown except in training, let alone a long distance. I glanced at Billy. He shook his head, almost imperceptibly, so I said nothing.

We were given directions to the aerodrome and, once we were safely away from the office, Billy grabbed my arm. "Can you believe it?" he said. "We're officers! Just like that! And to top it off we get to fly a fighter. On our own!"

"Well, *Flight Lieutenant* Miller," I said. "Do you know anything about a Sopwith 1½ Strutter?"

"No!" he exclaimed. "Who cares? We'll figure it out! We're pilots."

I groaned. "The Sopwith Strutter can do over a hundred miles per hour. At thirteen thousand feet it can still do over ninety. It's a much more powerful machine than the Jenny."

"Good," Billy grunted.

I gave him a punch. "I'm as excited as you are. I'm just suggesting you need to be cautious."

"How can you be cautious in war?" Billy asked.

* * *

We found lodging for the night, but neither of us slept well, with so much anticipation building for the coming day.

The next morning we arrived at the RNAS aerodrome at Hendon. It was nothing like Curtiss. It was a station made for war. The guard at the entrance looked over our papers meticulously. Another guard kept a close eye on us, as did soldiers in a tower on the opposite side of the compound.

I froze at the sight of ten planes on the dirt strip ahead of us. Five of them were Strutters: three bombers and two fighters. The guns mounted on the fighters made me think of Mr. Martin's warning about how different our experience in Europe would be than in Canada.

"That's them," I murmured.

"Absolutely posh!" Billy exclaimed.

A soldier walked up to us and saluted smartly. "This way please, sirs." We returned the salute. He took us to a hut and introduced us to the wing commander on duty.

"You're the Canadians then, are you?" the commander asked. "Miller, Townend? Good. Are you reasonably rested?"

We hadn't had that much sleep in the last 24 hours, but I wasn't about to raise the issue.

"Very reasonably, sir," Billy said.

"Victuals?"

"We could certainly do with some coffee, sir," Billy answered.

"Have you flown a Strutter?"

I answered this time. "No, sir. But we are familiar with them, sir."

"Good." He glanced at his pocket watch. "Find yourselves some sandwiches and coffee at the mess. The planes are fuelled. Take these papers to the officer on the field. You'll be given your gear, maps and directions there." He saluted us. "Have a good flight, lieutenants."

We were given flight gear, a little warmer than what we'd had in Toronto, and food. Our general instructions were to follow the coast some 300 miles, all the way to Redcar. We were to keep our eyes open for the towns of Ipswich and Great

Yarmouth, which would act as landmarks for us. We were to refuel at Grimsby, just south of the Humber River. There were ocean bays to watch out for as well, and we were warned to be ready for heavy wind while crossing them. The officer made notes on the map itself, outlining further land features.

"If you get lost," an officer told us, "set down safely and get your bearings from the nearest town. Don't hurt my planes!"

The Sopwith 1½ Strutter was a fantastic machine. It was the first British plane to have synchronized machine guns, allowing the pilot to shoot *through* the propeller blades. From what the field officer told us, these had only recently been installed.

"You shouldn't need them, I dare say," he told us. "But one can never be too sure. The Hun has been running us amuck recently. Their Zeppelins have been giving the public the most frightful turns. Bombs in the middle of the night and what have you. Keep your eyes peeled for those blighters. And for the sake of all of us, if you see one, bring it down!" He made the sign of the cross.

I took a long look at the Strutter and smiled. The reason for its name suddenly became clear to me: unlike the Jenny, one set of smaller struts connected the upper wing and the fuselage. The other struts connected solely from wing to wing. The fuselage struts looked half the size of the ones on the wings. She looked fast and more powerful than the Jenny. Despite my lack of experience, I could hardly wait to see what the plane could do.

I climbed in and noticed that it was a single-seater, whereas Billy's was a double. There was a Vickers machine gun mounted for the gunner on Billy's plane, in addition to one for the pilot. It sent a chill down my spine to see its shadow splayed across the grass. Billy looked at it too. He raised his eyebrows. Our days of learning to fly for the sheer enjoyment of flight were over. From now on we would train to kill.

From the moment the engine roared into life I could feel the difference in power compared to the Jenny. The Strutter wanted to be in the air! She tugged hard at the blocks and I sensed immediately that I needed to be more aggressive than I had in training.

We had a horse on the farm that Sarah named Bully. Bully was strong-willed, powerful and had to be kept firmly under control. The similarity between her and the Strutter was so striking that I caught myself saying, "Easy now, easy girl," before we left the blocks.

A glance over at Billy revealed that he was ready

too. He gave me a wave. I couldn't see his face, for it was completely covered by a cold-weather mask.

The ground crew removed the blocks and I edged my plane forward. The sun shone brightly as I headed out for the field. To the west I could see dark clouds and I wondered if we would run into them before long. I glanced back to see Billy a hundred yards behind and on my left. I held the stick firmly, prepared the flaps and then opened the throttle. The Strutter's speed was thrilling. Although the field was a little rougher than at Curtiss, I was able to lift off earlier than I had with the Jenny.

I played with the wings a little and felt the quick response to my command. I checked my gauges and watched my altitude as I climbed, to make sure all was in working order, precisely as Mr. Martin had taught me. Billy pulled alongside and dipped his wings in salute. It was the first time we had flown side by side. I raised my hand to him.

My eyes fell on the Vickers gun in front of me. I reached out and gripped the handle, allowing my finger to slip against the trigger. Was the safety on? No one had said anything about that. On the farm, our shotgun had a safety catch that had to be removed before you could fire it. The Vickers had a safety mechanism as well, a short bar that ran below the gun and ended in a knob-like handle. I gave the handle a push. It didn't move. I gave it a harder push and it suddenly clicked forward. But was it on or off?

"Bang, bang!" I shouted, imagining an enemy in my sights. The Strutter lurched with a sudden updraft of wind and I accidently squeezed the trigger.

Bang! Bang! Bang! Bang! Four shots rang out above the noise of the engine. I gaped, unbelieving, at the gun. Beside me, Billy just stared. When I recovered from my shock I looked at him and he slapped his forehead. Then he pointed to the gun in front of him and shook his hand across it. *No more.* I nodded. He didn't need to tell me. For some ridiculous reason I had assumed that the guns were not loaded. The field officer had said we wouldn't need them. He did *not* say they weren't ready for action. It was a sober reminder that our real work was to shoot down an enemy.

We made for the coast following the Thames River and right out to the eastern end of the Strait of Dover. I did not consult my maps until we reached the sea, as I wanted to spend some time exploring the Strutter.

Seeing England from the air was an extraordinary, surreal experience. Everything became

46

clearer, and the ocean, hills, towns and rivers were put into a more complete perspective. Yet as we kept flying, everything began to look the same. Each town had the same colouring as the next and the shapes of the rivers and streams were often hidden by forest or buildings.

I felt some panic as we made our way east to the sea and I pulled out my map. I had to look down and keep the paper flat against my knees to shield it from the wind. If my map blew away we'd be in for some trouble, for Billy didn't have as good a sense of direction as I did. I peered out over the cockpit and searched the coast below. There was an island ahead that looked something like a rhino's horn, with a river running north of it. Foulness Island. I put my map away and gave Billy a thumbs-up.

As we flew over Harwich, heading north, we had our first real scare. Billy pointed down, so I strained to see what he was looking at. In the harbour were two warships, making their way out to sea. We decided to go and have a closer look. No sooner had we descended when a puff of smoke appeared from the mainland. A split second later there was a booming sound and I suddenly realized they were shooting at *us*!

I banked sharply and increased altitude, and nearly put the Strutter into a stall. Billy was right

47

on my tail. I couldn't believe they had fired at us. Why on earth had they done that? I glanced back and saw that one of the ships had opened fire as well. Puffs of smoke, like tiny clouds, rose from her deck. Could they reach us from here? I took no chances and rose even higher, all the while increasing throttle to gain more distance.

As my heart settled I suddenly remembered that the town of Great Yarmouth, a short way up the coast, had been bombed last year, killing two people. No wonder they'd fired on us. It was possible that the Harwich port defence and sailors on the ships couldn't see the British insignia on our wings. We needed to be more careful.

Billy waved at me wildly. I knew he was grinning from ear to ear under his mask. I shuddered, and shook off the tension running through me. My hand was frozen to the control stick and I forced myself to relax. I took a deep breath. And then I chuckled and waved back at Billy. It was the first action we had seen. Only we hadn't counted on being shot at by our own side!

* * *

I was low on fuel. The trouble had started just after we reached The Wash, the enormous bay south of Skegness. The clouds were now billowing and grey. It was terribly disorienting. I tried to keep

48

a straight course, but soon found that using the water as a marker was not enough. I needed to see the coastline in order to be sure of our bearings.

I had to keep wiping my goggles. Huge curtains of cloud floated between our two planes and I lost sight of Billy. I let go of the control stick for a moment and turned right around to check. He was gone. I slammed the side of the cockpit with my fist, but maintained speed and direction, hoping that he would pop through the clouds any second.

I resisted the temptation to turn back. If either of us changed course in any way, there was no hope of finding one another in such massive clouds. I banked very gently a few times port and starboard in the hope of catching sight of him, but all I accomplished was losing fuel.

I needed to drop beneath the clouds to get my bearings. I could only hope that Billy would do the same. I pushed the control stick forward and descended.

The moment I came clear of the clouds, I realized how dangerous the situation was. I was headed for open sea at 60 miles per hour and low on fuel. At my present course I'd run out of fuel and crash into the ocean. I turned sharply back for the shore.

It didn't take me long to find my way. The officer

back at the RNAS base had written *Clock Tower* on my map at the town of Skegness. Flying at 1500 feet, I saw the tower and gave a shout of triumph — only 40 miles or so to Grimsby, where we were to refuel. I peered at the fuel gauge. Close to the low mark, but still a little left. I searched constantly for Billy, and prayed for him too. I pushed away the thought of him flying far above me and heading straight out to sea for a watery death.

I was coming up on a small town, which I presumed was Saltfleet, when I spotted Billy. He was below me and less than a mile ahead. Not daring to increase throttle with so little fuel left, I descended to his altitude. To my amazement, I caught up with him in a few minutes. He waved happily, as if nothing was amiss. I held up both my hands and shook my head. *Where did you go?*

He tapped his fuselage and showed a thumbs-down. I nodded. We were now 10 miles out from Grimsby. I thought back to my training sessions with Mr. Martin and Mr. Edwards. Only once had we landed without fuel and it was Mr. Martin who was at the controls. I reviewed in my mind what our manuals said about landing without power.

I was still wrestling with possibilities when the mouth of the Humber River came into view. There were the towns of Cleethorpes and Grimsby. I caught Billy's attention and he followed me down. Just past Cleethorpes my engine began to sputter. I lowered the nose to see if I could direct the last of the fuel to the engine. Then I waved frantically at Billy. He eased up on the throttle and came in behind me.

At around 1000 feet the engine quit and my propeller stopped. My stomach lurched as the Strutter lost power. The sudden quiet was disconcerting. Billy moved alongside. He pointed to a farmer's field not far from the town. I aimed for the brown patch, hoping desperately that the farmer had removed any large rocks or stumps from his field.

The ground approached quickly. Suddenly, as I dipped my wings for a better view, I caught sight of a rock wall at the foot of the field.

"Damn!" I shouted, and adjusted my flaps for more lift. There was only one shot at landing and I could not pull up to try again. The wall was sickeningly close. I squeezed my eyes shut as the top of the wall went under me. I missed it by a hair. Seconds later I touched down and bumped violently along, all the while trying to keep the nose straight. Something yellow and grey suddenly appeared in front of me. There was no time to turn so I threw my hands in front of my face. The

51

Strutter staggered for a moment and then carried right *through* the obstacle. The plane came to rest after a final jolt. Bits of straw covered the fuselage and hung down in front of my eyes. I had struck a whole stack of it!

I climbed out and leapt down off the bottom wing. Billy walked towards me shaking his head. "You're the luckiest dog I've ever met!" he said. "You managed to hit the only haystack that wasn't loaded into the barn. Soaking wet too. Stopped you without tearing the plane to pieces. And you missed a stone fence by three feet at the most. I thought I was going to have to pick up pieces of you."

His own plane had touched down with fuel still in the tank. Whether it was because he'd descended earlier and lost less time in the clouds, or because he'd kept his speed down, we didn't know.

We walked around the plane searching for any damage.

"Not a scratch!" exclaimed Billy.

"Not quite," I said. The tail guard had broken off. We lifted the tail and Billy ran his hand underneath. "Pretty clean break. You'll have to have someone to hold the tail up until takeoff. I'll do it if we can't find anyone else."

I glanced across the field to a stone farmhouse sitting a half mile away at the top of a low hill.

"Maybe up there?" I said. "And where are we going to refuel? And how will we get fuel out to this field?"

We made our way up to the farmhouse. We needn't have worried about knocking. Three figures were already making their way down to us. One of them carried a shotgun. When we were within a hundred yards of them, the tallest figure raised his gun above our heads and fired. We ducked and then froze in our steps.

"Who needs to go to France?" Billy muttered. "We can just stay here and be shot by our own side. Twice in one day."

"We're friends!" I shouted. "Pilots. My plane crashed."

"Where might you be from, then?" the middle one asked.

"Canada!" shouted Billy. "And for goodness' sake, please point that thing somewhere else. We're not pheasants!"

The farmer lowered his gun. "All right then," came the reply. "If you're under the king, that's the main thing."

Once our identity was settled, the farmer and his family treated us like royalty. One of the boys was sent to hitch up a wagon to take us into town.

"You'll stay and take a meal with us and then

we'll get you to town," the farmer said. We were taken inside. Billy was in his element and soon had the farmer, whose name was Timpson, laughing as he told stories about his own farm back in Winnipeg.

A girl came into the room carrying a jug and mugs. She was no more than a year or two younger than me, but was the prettiest girl I'd ever seen in my life.

"Nellie," Mr. Timpson said. "See if the wagon's come 'round."

Nellie, I thought. *Nellie Timpson.* It was a name worth remembering. As she set down a mug in front of me she flashed me a smile.

"Thank . . . thanks, Miss," I stammered.

Billy leaned forward and said charmingly, "I believe my friend is thanking you for the coffee and for your smile." I blushed to the roots of my hair. Mr. Timpson laughed and slapped Billy on the shoulder. I didn't follow the rest of the conversation very well. I kept glancing out the doorway to catch a glimpse of Nellie.

Mr. Timpson gave us a ride into town and Nellie was allowed to ride with us. Billy nudged me and whispered, "Sit in the back, you ninny." He climbed up beside the farmer and immediately began telling a story about a horse they had. Nellie and I sat with our legs dangling over the edge of the wagon. She did most of the talking, which suited me just fine, as I wanted to listen to her voice.

"What about your family, then?" she asked after a while.

She nodded when I spoke about my brother fighting in France. "The boys are a bit young yet," she said, speaking of her own brothers. "It won't be long though," she added. "I dread the day." She was quiet for a moment and then looked at me. "What about you, Paul? Aren't you afraid of being killed?"

For a moment I was tempted to tell her that I wasn't. Instead, I said, "Sometimes I'm scared out of my mind." I glanced at her to see if she thought less of me, but she gave no indication other than a kind smile. So I said, "I sing hymns, and that seems to help. When I'm in the clouds it seems natural to pray for courage." I thought for a moment. "Robert told me once to always move towards the fear." I stared at my feet. "I try to do that. But he's always been the brave one."

She suddenly put her hand on mine and said, "I think brave people are scared like anyone else. It's just that they do something to help in the heat of trouble. Even if 'tisn't glorious. And you're here, Paul. You're in England, in a flying machine.

Even though you're scared. That's something already, isn't it?"

We were quiet for a time and then I asked, "Nellie, may I write to you?"

She nodded. "I will write back every time you do. And I'll pray for you each day." We talked the whole way to the base. I'd never spoken that long to any of the girls I'd met at church or school.

* * *

As much as I was excited to be back in the Strutter, there was a part of me that wanted to stay longer and talk with Nellie. The army sent a truck to refuel the plane, fix the tail section and help with takeoff. Mr. Timpson's whole family stood in the field to watch. Nellie stepped back so no one would see and blew me a kiss. I jumped into the cockpit as if I had springs on the bottom of my feet.

Once we were in the air I could not resist flying low over the field with Billy right on my tail. I waved and watched the figures disappear behind me.

From Grimsby we made our way without incident to Redcar, and this time I brought the Strutter down smoothly, taking extra care of the patched-up tail. The ground crew met us and held the plane steady as I switched off the engine.

"G'day, sir," said a crewman as he saluted me. He raised his eyebrows at the patched tail guard. "Had a bit of bad luck on your way here?"

"Ran out of fuel just before Grimsby," I answered. "We had to land in a field." But it wasn't unlucky at all. I'd met Nellie.

After a good night's rest we began our training in earnest. As it turned out, we were the only Canadians left. Our mates from Hut C had already been sent to France. Our new companions were British officers, and the difference between us was evident immediately. All of them came from wealthier families than our own. I was afraid to open my mouth around these well-mannered, clever men. I doubted if any of them had milked a cow. Nonetheless, they were very good to us, and helpful in sorting out how things operated at the aerodrome. All of them respected us for already having our pilot's licences. Several of them had been on hand when we landed from Grimsby and were impressed by our handling of the Strutters.

One of the most exciting bits of training was machine-gun practice. There was a tiny rail track installed at the far end of the aerodrome with a little cart that ran along it. The cart had a chair and a fixed gun, much the same as the one on Billy's Strutter. On the hillside were various targets. Our objective was to try to hit the targets while sitting in the moving rail car. We each took turns. While it was deafening, I found it enjoyable to watch the line of bullets getting closer and closer to the target until I finally struck it. Only later did I think of how those bullets might soon be aimed at a real enemy.

That night, instead of writing to Sarah or Robert, I wrote to Nellie. It had only been a day since I'd crash-landed on the farm, and yet I found I already had so much to tell her. I sketched a picture at the bottom of the page of her family saying goodbye to us. I drew her hand in the act of blowing a kiss. Beside her figure in the picture I wrote: *Right back at you!*

* * *

Our flight instructors began our training in warfare in the skies. They showed us detailed diagrams of airships — dirigibles, or Zeppelins, as the Germans called them. These massive rigid airships could sail over the English Channel and drop bombs on major cities or military targets. Part of our role at Redcar was to hunt for the Zeppelins along the coast while on dawn patrol.

There was also the possibility of enemy bombers coming over the Channel, so we learned about some of the planes the Germans were flying. Our flight instructor presented a picture of the Albatros and I remembered Mr. Martin's sharp words to Billy. My general sense of the instructor's lesson was that new machines and inventions for flying were cropping up daily. Both sides were working night and day to create superior airplanes.

One afternoon an instructor approached Billy and me while the officers were having a smoke break. "Listen, you fellows," he said. "I want you to head up and play a little game of tag in the air."

I stared at him blankly. "I want the fellows to witness the art of escape and chase," he finished.

Billy and I exchanged glances. "Yes, sir," I responded.

The instructor turned to Billy and said sternly, "Don't hurt the machines!"

It was good to be up in the air again. We had agreed to warm up a bit and then play a little chase. We had never tried it before, and the only time one of us had flown behind the other was on our ferry to Redcar. After a turn or two I looked behind me and suddenly found Billy right on my tail. The game had begun. I gained altitude and decided to give our friends on the ground a show. I took the Strutter into a loop and Billy followed. The powerful engine took me right into the loop, but it somehow seemed different than the Jenny. The

Strutter felt stronger and yet more reactive too — as if a single touch of the controls would send the machine spinning into a roll.

I also noticed that my goggles were clouded. I wiped at them with my gloves and saw what appeared to be oil stains. The smell of oil and petrol had been present the entire flight, but now I noticed a dark spray coming from the engine from time to time. After a second wipe I could see clearly again. Mr. Martin had mentioned castor oil back in Toronto and now I knew what he meant.

I banked port and starboard but could not shake Billy. It was as if he could predict my every move. Had we been in a real battle and he opened fire, my plane would have been ripped to shreds. I thought of what to do next and then remembered one of the diagrams they had shown us on the chart. I climbed again and went into a loop. Billy was right with me. This time, however, as I was coming out of the last part of the loop, I banked sharply to starboard.

The manoeuvre caught Billy by surprise and he kept going straight. I followed the turn and came around behind him. He shook his fist at me playfully. I waved. We took a few more turns and then landed.

Once we were on the ground again, the flight instructor approached us a second time. "Well done, lads. A fine turn, Mr. Townend, I do say. However, you will find that many such manoeuvres may be required in a single dogfight."

"Planes are safe and sound, sir." Billy grinned.

"So I see," replied the instructor. "Let's hope your luck keeps rolling, shall we?" He smiled, not unkindly, and said, "You're on dawn patrol tomorrow."

Chapter 5
October 1916

The next day, Billy and I participated in our first dawn patrol. Four of us went up while it was still dark, one after the other taking to the skies. It was terrifying in those first few minutes before the grey light of dawn appeared. I kept my nose aimed at the elusive shadow of our leader, Williams, a gruff British officer. We knew that the main reason for our turn on dawn patrol was to practise formation, and Williams was the man to teach us. Not long into the patrol we spotted a Zeppelin. It was out of range for us, yet the very sight of that giant airship with its black Iron Cross set my heart racing.

"Make note of when and where we saw it," Williams said sternly when we were back on the ground.

Writing reports was part of our daily work. Time, altitude, speed, towns — all had to be recorded in logbooks. It was tedious, unfulfilling work, especially when absolutely nothing happened on most of our sorties. Yet after our brief encounter with the Zeppelin, I realized the importance of the log-books. Our report put the coast on high alert. Lives were at stake: not only those in the air but civilians on the ground. I thought of Nellie and her family. What could they do against bombs dropped from high above? A warning allowed them to find some protection in the cellar. And what about Robert, hunkered down in some trench with bombs landing all around him? I was angry just thinking about it. It made me want to go straight back up and hunt the Zeppelin down.

That afternoon the mail arrived and I gave a whoop of joy when the carrier held up two letters for me. One was from my mother with a note and a letter from Robert folded inside. The other was from Nellie. I didn't know where to start!

I opened Robert's crinkled letter. The seal was in place — that meant that my mother had not opened it. Whatever my brother said to me was for my eyes only. I began to read.

He had seen action. A lot of it. I read on. As pilots, we all heard stories of the harsh life at the Front. Billy had chosen flying instead of infantry for that very reason. And what Robert described was horrible. Three of his friends had been lost in a single charge, shot down like a row of pigeons on a fence. Gone was his excitement. Gone was his enthusiasm. Small wonder, when Canadian casualties had been so high recently at the Somme, in particular at the village of Courcelette.

Between the lines of his words I sensed a creeping despair. But then I smiled grimly. His courage was still there. His last lines read: *We'll get them yet. Be safe, little brother.*

In my mother's note she mentioned that Robert had received news of my enlistment and pilot training from Sarah. She said he honoured my choice and that, God willing, we would meet in France. I set the letter down, allowing my mind to drift back to our farm, my parents and Sarah.

"All's well?" Billy sat down beside me.

"It's rough going at the Front," I said. I didn't want to say too much, knowing what had happened to his brother.

"That it is," he murmured.

I held up Nellie's letter. He tried to snatch it from me. "You dog!" he cried with a grin. I wanted privacy to read it and without another word Billy wandered off.

Her writing was neat and simple like Sarah's, which suddenly made me wonder about her schooling. Her family was well. She had received my letter and was delighted with my drawings. To my surprise she included her own drawing: a small sketch of a biplane, so high it looked almost like a bird, and of an arm and hand just entering the frame and waving from the ground. She had drawn something floating between the hand and the plane and I realized that it was a kiss. I tucked Nellie's letter into my jacket pocket, right next to my maps.

Over the next few days we practised target shooting more than usual and discussed how to attack a Zeppelin. We also received a short stint of training on how to escort Strutter bombers.

* * *

Williams came to our hut one night after supper. "Be on the ready, lads," he said. "Word has it we might be flying tonight. An unconfirmed sighting of an airship off Whitby. Looks like the Hun is back."

Twenty minutes later he returned. "To your planes!" he commanded. I scrambled off my bunk and into my gear. Two of the lads who weren't flying tonight jumped up and helped us with zippers and gloves. It was the first time we had been called to a sortie from the ground with an actual enemy in sight, and everyone was excited.

It was an unusually cold night. Billy clapped my shoulder as we ran to our planes. "Good luck, Paul. I've got your back."

"And same for you," I said.

We took off in staggered intervals, a few minutes between each plane to avoid collisions once we were up there. The first few minutes in the air were more terrifying than dawn patrol, for the darkness never left. There were moments when I was completely blind, relying solely on hearing. I strained to see ahead. I sang a hymn to keep my heart from pounding so hard.

The moon crept out from the clouds and the world changed. It was a little like entering a room with a candle: directly ahead was silver and clear, while beside and below remained in darkness. Clouds floated past us like elusive shadows — blimp-like shapes appearing and disappearing in the sky.

I reached forward and touched my Vickers gun nervously. If it jammed, I had no defence other than my flying skills. My hand trembled as I touched the gun handle. I didn't touch the trigger, having learned my lesson from my first flight in a Strutter.

I found the Zeppelin just north of Whitby. The towns were blacked out — all their lights extinguished so the airships could not find targets on the ground. However, I knew from my speed and flying time that Whitby was close.

It was a larger airship than the one I'd followed previously. The sight of it made me shiver. The Zeppelin had not yet spotted me, for it maintained its course rather than increasing altitude. They would hear us soon enough.

Over the next 10 minutes I slowly climbed higher, searching for my companions. The sky was bright enough for me to catch glints here and there, and I realized I was not alone. One or two others had also spotted the Zeppelin. Our objective, as determined back at the base, was to rise above the dirigible and fire down on it. The moon illuminated the giant cylindrical shape enough that I could see the forward and aft gondolas clearly. It was from these compartments that our greatest challenge would come.

There were at least two other Strutters with me. The moonlight glinted from time to time off their wings. My heart pounded as we drew closer.

We pulled even with the airship at about 9000 feet and were still climbing to get above it when the crew spotted us. The ceiling was low and we soon pulled clear of the clouds and into the full moonlit sky. Their guns opened up. Red flames suddenly appeared from the aft gondola as their gunners fired. Bullets whined through the air around me and a small hole appeared in my top wing. I banked sharply away from the airship.

For a brief moment I felt the urge to keep on going, to head straight back to the aerodrome. Then

I heard Robert's words in my mind: *Move towards the fear.* I cleared the castor oil from my goggles and took a breath. "Okay," I said. "Here we go."

When I came around again, the Zeppelin's nose was angled upward as it tried to gain altitude and escape our attack. The moment I was within 1000 feet of it, bullets whizzed around me again. I fired a burst and then stopped immediately as Billy's plane shot by my nose. "Billy!" I screamed. "I almost shot you!" The tracer bullets continued to follow his plane like hellish fireflies in the night.

Suddenly the giant sides of the airship were right in front of me. I pulled back hard on the stick. The engine strained and my poor Strutter shook like a rag doll. "Come on, come *on!*" I muttered. A second later I was clear of the Zeppelin and headed for open sky. I hoped that none of my companions was above me, for it was still difficult to see.

Instead of pulling out from the stall, I kept my nose up and performed a loop. Once again the Strutter shook and shimmied. At the end of the manoeuvre I maintained a dive and saw the enormous top of the airship some 700 feet in front of me. At 500 feet I opened fire. Orange and blue flame erupted from my guns as the red streaks of my incendiary bullets headed for the airship's top.

As I pulled away and got ready for another loop,

I caught sight of a streaking flame off the starboard side of the Zeppelin. Another Strutter. The plane's nose turned towards the earth and it began to spiral, with billows of white smoke filling its wake.

"No!" I cried. I levelled my Strutter and leaned out, straining to see the burning plane. There was no way of telling whose it was. Suddenly I was furious at the Zeppelin. I pulled hard on the stick and ignored the pressure and buffeting wind. I hardly even noticed when I turned upside down this time. All I could think of was seeing the top of the airship again.

I managed to fire two bursts into the top of the Zeppelin. Ahead of me was another plane, strafing its aft portion. I pulled up just as an orange glow appeared at the airship's midsection. Its gunners had stopped firing. I gained some distance and then turned around. A blast of flame roared out from the top as the Zeppelin exploded. I watched, fascinated, until the hot air struck my Strutter. My wings were buffeted so fiercely I was afraid they would be torn off. There was nothing I could do to break free. All I could do was fight to keep her steady and wait for the buffeting to pass.

When the blast ended I regained control and turned back. The dark night revealed a hideous sight. The frame of the dying Zeppelin stood out starkly in the yellow and orange flames, like the skeleton of a giant beast as it fell through the skies. Small figures, like sparks, fell off from the burning mass and blazed tiny trails to the ground. With horror I realized that they were men.

"Lord have mercy," I murmured. I felt sick to my stomach.

The remaining Strutters were ahead of me. I caught up quickly, suddenly remembering the burning plane I had seen earlier. Billy waved at me in the bright moonlight and I leaned back heavily in my seat, whispering thanks. On closer inspection it appeared that Williams was the one who had gone down. I thought for a moment that I was going to vomit into my mask. Billy suddenly dipped his wings and took the lead, heading towards the ground and not our aerodrome. We followed him as best we could, keeping a safe distance, making our way home.

Here and there along the ground we saw burning pieces of the Zeppelin. The main body had fallen into the sea only a hundred yards from shore.

I scanned the ground as best I could, still trying to spot Williams, but it was difficult to see anything. When we finally touched down, I sat in the cockpit for several minutes after the engine stopped.

"Sir?" a ground crewman ventured.

"It's all right," I heard Billy say. "I've got him." He climbed onto the wing and sat on the edge of the cockpit. "I don't think Williams is dead, Paul," he said. "I saw him level out. The light was tricky, but I swear he gained control. And then the flames went out and I couldn't see him anymore. That's why I brought us so close to the ground."

I couldn't believe my ears. "You're sure?"

"I've already informed ground crew," Billy said. "They'll send a wire to Whitby and the search will be on."

We were silent for a moment and then I said, "Billy, what have we done? Those men . . . those burning men."

He gripped my shoulder. "You listen to me, Paul Townend! The men in that Zeppelin were about to drop bombs on women and children! On girls like your Nellie. You remember *that*!" He pushed me roughly and started to leave.

"Billy, wait!" I released my safety belt and stood up. "We blew the Zeppelin wide open. I've never killed anything other than a chicken. And these were *men*. I don't know what to feel."

"Feel nothing," he said gruffly. "It's easier that way."

* * *

71

They brought Williams back the next morning. He was dead. They found his plane at the edge of a field outside of Whitby. He must have managed to bring the plane down under control, only to strike a tree in the darkness. The commander asked Billy to write a letter informing Williams's parents, as Billy was the last to see him go down.

"You're better with words, Paul," he said, and pushed the paper towards me.

I nodded. It was the most difficult thing I had ever written. My hand shook when I picked up the pen. Williams was twenty-one years old and their only son.

That night at supper Billy stood up at the table in the mess hall. He raised his glass and all conversation stopped. "To Williams," he said simply. There was a murmur of assent and all raised their glasses. After a pause Billy added, "Grieve, but don't weep. You can't shoot the Hun with tears in your eyes."

Later, when I reached the end of my letter, my hand finally stopped shaking.

Chapter 6
Mid-October 1916

Two days later, four of us were transferred to No. 3 Wing RNAS and given orders to ferry two Sopwith 1½ Strutter bombers and two fighters to Luxeuil air base in eastern France.

Flying across the English Channel was a monumental experience. It was considered a rite of passage. We left from Whitefield, near Dover, where I traded my single-seater for a two-seater fighter. The bombers were loaded and we all shook hands before taking off. Billy clapped my shoulder. "Here we go, Paulie! *Au revoir! À bientôt!*"

It was cold and the high winds whipped up the water below into a crisp chop. There were no clouds, though. Once again I felt the emotional combination of exhilaration and fear. We were flying towards France and the front lines of battle and not the relative safety of our aerodrome at Redcar. Flying escort for the bombers meant that we were their eyes and ears, their protectors. I didn't have the security of three other fighters in tight formation ready to come to my aid when I needed it. It also crossed my mind that I was getting closer to Robert. Once in France, I would try to find out where he was fighting.

While Redcar had been a considerable change from Curtiss, the difference between England and Luxeuil was another huge step. The most evident difference was the number of planes — French and British planes, whole squadrons of them parked on the airstrip. We found ourselves sharing the airfield with several squadrons, including American fighter pilots from the famous French Escadrille Americaine, designated N.124.

"Well, this is something," Billy murmured as we surveyed the scene. "I suppose we have finally arrived at the war." We soon noticed a feeling among the flyers here that was different from Redcar. Men returned to their huts at the end of the day looking haggard, and there was less laughter.

For several days we practised escorting bombers, and Billy and I were assigned gunners. Harry Pritchard, from Nova Scotia, sat in the cockpit behind me. In only a few short hours of training we developed plenty of communication signals in preparation for combat.

We heard the guns from the Front that night, an incessant booming sound, very faint, that must have been shockingly loud nearby. I wondered about Robert and if he was right in the middle of it all, or if his unit was somewhere safe. In the morning there was fog, and we stood ready for an hour or so in case it lifted. The clouds settled in, however, and there was no flying. Instead, Billy, Harry and I walked into the town of Luxeuil. I wanted to see the old Benedictine monastery, but Harry thought we ought to get back to base. We did stop for coffee at a little café with the hills in full view. I drew a picture of the centre of town for Nellie that night.

Some days later, on a clear, cold morning, we stood ready for a scheduled raid. We were headed across enemy lines, where our bombers were to target a munitions factory. Billy and I wished each other luck.

This would be the most dangerous sortie we had yet attempted — actually attacking the enemy over enemy lines. Harry whistled as we walked to our plane. It was a nervous little tune and I wished that he would keep silent. We shook hands once we were in our seats.

"Good luck, Paul!" he said.

"You too," I answered. My mind was already turned to the start-up routine. I checked the gauges and tried the ailerons. Thirteen other planes started up around me, Billy's included. The noise was deafening, and as we pulled away from our blocks, clouds of dust blew across the airstrip. It was quite a contingent compared to the few planes of dawn patrol. We kept the bombers at our centre. Billy, Ashcroft, Watson and I formed a Canadian right flank.

Ashcroft was a tall, sandy-haired man from Ontario. I liked him well enough, as did Billy, and the three of us had formed an alliance on the soccer field the last game or two. I had not met Watson until the night before. He kept to himself for the most part. He was from Saskatchewan.

We climbed to 10,000 feet and then flew steadily northeast, heading for the German border. Even though we were bundled up in winter gear, my hands were cold. I realized shortly that it was my nerves and not the temperature causing my discomfort. I shook my shoulders and tried to relax.

I was not the only one feeling anxious. Usually when we flew in formation, Billy allowed his wings to dip or slide playfully with updrafts. On this raid he kept his plane reined in, pulling the nose down quickly and straightening his wings as if containing a spirited horse.

The visibility was excellent. I searched the skies around me, knowing that Harry was doing the same. The towns beneath us were difficult to distinguish, each with its own churches and steeples. We relied more on landmarks such as lakes and hills and their proximity to determine particular towns. We had all been briefed on our flight plan, but it was the leaders of the formation who were doing the navigating; they would be closely following the maps.

About an hour out from our base we tightened formation. We were getting close. The bombers began to descend. I realized that we were fully behind German lines. I glanced back at Harry and found him sitting alert, with his hands firmly placed on the guns.

The land came more clearly into focus and I was surprised to find farmers' fields and crisscross fences that looked the same as they did in France. Somehow the Germans had become so much of an enemy that I had forgotten they had farms, farmers, families. I hated the thought that we might be dropping bombs near these civilians.

Our target was a cleared area with a set of buildings in the middle, steam rising from a row of chimney stacks. A number of trucks travelled the road leading from the woods to the factory.

Our bombers did their work, dropping bomb after bomb in succession. We stayed right with them and then banked for a second turn. Ashcroft gave me a wave — partially, I think, to share the bizarre experience going on below. We were present but not really participating.

It was surreal to see the bombs explode. No sooner did they touch the ground than enormous sheets of earth were hurled into the air. Half a building crumpled and the bricks spilled like toy blocks onto the ground. Smoke soon covered the area and I could not tell if our strike was successful or not, but I did see two trucks rise right up into the air and land on their sides. One of the wheels ended up on the remaining portion of the factory roof. I couldn't help smiling — it was such a strange sight. I was glad for the smoke, however, for there were no bodies or dying men to see, as there had been with the Zeppelin.

Flickering light from below caught my attention. There were flames now, leaping up beneath the smoke. And then it was all over. Not a single shot was fired at us. We made one last pass and then we were on our way back to France like a swift-moving storm, striking and flowing past. Ashcroft pulled up alongside me and pointed to the skies around us: *Watch carefully!*

We gained altitude in the hope of seeing enemy sorties before they saw us. Billy saluted me as we came back into formation. Harry kept looking beneath us and behind, sometimes standing up for a better view. Ashcroft, Watson, Billy and I took up the rear guard to cover our retreat.

Not more than 10 minutes passed before we were attacked. They came from above, dropping down on us like hawks chasing sparrows. I didn't even know they were on us until Harry's gun started chugging away. He had no time to warn me. The first Albatros sped between Billy and me in a dive and I realized in a second that he was preparing to loop. So did Billy. We both pushed down on our control sticks to follow, and opened fire. I fired burst after burst. Brushing too close to Billy, I pulled up and edged portside, unable to follow the Albatros. I had to get back to the bombers and provide them some cover.

"Hold on, Harry!" I shouted. "I'm taking us back."

Bullets whined through the canvas of my top wing. An Albatros had slipped in just behind us. "Shoot, Harry!" I shouted.

Glancing over my shoulder, I saw the checkered plane swing out wide from our tail and open fire again. Any closer and the Albatros would strike our fuselage. I banked sharply both to escape from the barrage and to catch a glimpse of our attacker. "Harry!" I shouted uselessly against the wind. "Shoot him!" Harry's gun remained silent and I could only guess that he was changing cartridges. I had to buy him time.

The Albatros was still right on our tail. I stayed in the turn and then glanced sharply behind to see how Harry was managing. He was slumped grotesquely over his gun.

More bullets whizzed around me, bringing me back sharply to the moment. I banked to starboard and downward, still unable to shake the Albatros, which stayed tight behind me. Only my constant turns kept the gunner from filling me full of holes. A couple of rough patches of air helped as well, for it was difficult to shoot accurately in the turbulence. Still, he had already got Harry. The thought made me so angry I increased throttle and banked sharply. It was time to loop and turn my guns on the enemy. I was just about to dive when I saw Billy coming at me from my starboard side. He opened fire on the Albatros and then roared overhead. The pilot slumped and the German plane fell away with smoke billowing from its fuselage.

"You got him, Billy!" I shouted, raising my hands. "Don't you worry, Harry-boy. Billy took him down for you!"

We neared the French border and the German planes disengaged suddenly, pulling up and heading for home, probably low on fuel or unwilling to cross into enemy territory.

I rejoined Ashcroft behind the bombers. Billy joined us a moment later and I gave him a wave. Watson was missing and so was one of the bombers. The German attack had taken its toll. Ashcroft and his gunner shook their heads solemnly when they saw Harry. There was nothing I could do for him but bring him back to the aerodrome. He was still in his safety belt, so there was no danger of him falling out. At least I could bring his body back.

All the way home my mind was filled with images of our walk into Luxeuil the other day. I thought of Harry sipping his coffee, anxious for us to return to base. Anxious for what? A faster death? I said a prayer for him and for his family back in Nova Scotia.

Chapter 7
October–November 1916

We buried Harry in Luxeuil, in a graveyard near where we had taken our walk. A French priest said the eulogy. Harry was surrounded by all the pilots and gunners who had been on the bombing raid. Many others from the aerodrome walked in procession with us to the graveside. A few people from the town stood and watched. Afterwards I wrote a description of what had happened the day Harry died, and included a sketch of where he was buried in my letter to his parents.

I stared at the letter for some time and thought hard about Harry's death. I wondered again and again if we all should have been more vigilant. Harry had seen the enemy first. Perhaps if I had manoeuvred faster and gained altitude instead of banking away to escape, he might still be alive. The possibilities were endless. The horrible image of poor Harry slumped in his seat haunted me.

Billy came and sat by my bed on the night of the funeral. "What could I have done differently, Billy?" I asked.

"Nothing," he answered. "And don't be an idiot. It's not as if you ran away. You were firing just as hard as he was. It could easily have been you or me who took the bullet. We've been lucky so far. Harry's time was up. That's all you can say and then you put it behind you."

Robert had said the same thing. But it was not easy to stop thinking.

We found out several days later that Watson and his gunner had been killed as well. Their plane crashed behind enemy lines. A letter from a German pilot indicated that both men had been buried with honour.

Through the next few weeks, I wrote daily to Nellie, to my parents and Sarah, and more than ever to Robert, with Harry's death filling my thoughts.

Partly to take our minds off such deep losses, we also played a good deal of soccer when the weather permitted. The ground was hard, and before each match we picked up any of the larger stones. Regardless of our efforts to clean the field of rocks, I received more wounds from soccer than from flying, a fact for which I was eternally grateful.

One day I received a photograph from Nellie. It was a newspaper clipping showing her knitting socks for soldiers. Girls and women all over England were lending their knitting and stitching skills to help the war effort. The picture had been in my hands for hardly a minute when Ashcroft stole it and handed it to Billy, who ran out the door.

When I finally got hold of the picture I saw that someone had pencilled in, *Ooooh, Paulie! Look at me stitch*, on the margin. Billy swore that it wasn't him. And then he burst out laughing. "Ashcroft came up with a new name for you," he added when he recovered. "Stitch." The name stuck and from that moment on I was known as Stitch.

But that was one of the light moments in a difficult few weeks. One day an RNAS officer named Raymond and a reconnaissance photographer, Peters, went up to take some practice shots at the new aerodrome targets that had been set up so that pilots and gunners could practise shooting from various heights and angles. At barely 100 feet from takeoff the propeller cut out and the Strutter went into a nosedive. Raymond was killed instantly. He was only twenty. And Peters, who had simply gone up for the ride, was taken to hospital with what they assumed were internal injuries. And then Ashcroft wrecked the undercarriage of his plane — twice — while landing.

Even our ground crews were not exempt. One of the mechanics received a serious injury when the damaged undercarriage of a reconnaissance plane collapsed, pinning his legs.

I kept waiting for misfortune to strike. I did not have to wait long. Days later we received news that we were moving to a more forward position, to Ochey, a town near Tantonville. We were detailed to ferry our planes to the new base. Billy, Ashcroft and I set out on the same day. There was a skiff of snow on the ground, but the ceiling was quite high and there was little chance of precipitation.

As we made our way along, Ashcroft suddenly spotted enemy fighters. We were close to the border and I couldn't tell if they were on the French side or headed back to Germany. They changed course when they saw us, six of them, and turned in our direction. As they approached I recognized the Albatros and the Iron Cross insignia.

They came straight for us. Five hundred feet away they broke formation and roared past without firing a shot. As one of them flew parallel to my Strutter, he saluted me. I was so astonished I just stared as he went past. A moment later they came around again, now on our tails. Of all the cheek! Their first pass had simply been to get a good look at us! Billy increased throttle.

The German planes opened fire. I flitted from side to side to make myself a more difficult target.

With one more glance behind I banked sharply to port and opened fire as the Albatros passed by. He was so close that I could see bullet holes appear on his tail section.

Although I hit him several times, his plane remained on its course. The bullets had passed right through the wing and registered no fatal damage. The Albatros on my tail veered off to face Ashcroft, who had made a loop and returned to the fray. I looked all around to keep track of everyone near me. We were fighting so closely that a single miscalculation could put me directly in the line of fire of an enemy plane, or a collision with one of my own.

I increased throttle and turned to help Ashcroft. This time, on a hunch, I opened fire before the Albatros came fully into my view. While the first burst missed, the second found its mark. Holes appeared near the fuselage. Within seconds, smoke began to billow from the front of the plane.

There was no time to celebrate, for bullets whined around my cockpit once more. Suddenly something hit my shoulder and threw me forward. I wondered if the top wing had collapsed and landed at the base of my neck. Eventually I realized that I had been hit by a bullet. My first instinct was to touch the wound, but I resisted.

There was a plane coming at me from above and I needed to manoeuvre. I pushed the control stick forward and went into a dive. He followed. Using the speed from the dive, I manoeuvered into a loop and pulled back smoothly on the stick. The pain in my shoulder was unrelenting.

As I came around again I was stunned to see three German planes breaking off the attack. The plane chasing me also veered off. Far below, a smoking Albatros spiralled downward. The others sped towards it. Moments later the smoking plane pulled out of the spiral. There was no sign of the sixth plane.

Billy and Ashcroft pulled alongside me. Ashcroft pointed at me and then at his shoulder. I glanced down. Blood was soaking my coat. Now that my nerves had settled from the fight, I began to feel the pain even more acutely. I clamped my right hand down on my left shoulder and flew left-handed. Billy hovered anxiously. He made a fist. *Be strong!* I did not feel strong. I felt dizzy and sick.

For the rest of the flight, Billy and Ashcroft checked on me every few minutes. They flew parallel to my plane, one at a time, spelling each other off and giving a thumbs-up. I couldn't return the sign but I nodded. My hand felt frozen to the stick. My shoulder throbbed. I wondered if the bullet was lodged inside or had passed through. The thought made me woozy so I focused on Nellie. I thought of her sitting on the wagon and talking to me. In my last letter I'd promised to try and see her when I went on leave.

Ashcroft banked slowly to starboard and we began our descent. Twice I nearly passed out. It felt as if someone had stuck a pitchfork into my shoulder. In the last few minutes of our descent I could no longer hold the control stick with my left hand. I had to let go of my shoulder and steer with my right hand. Billy flicked his wings from time to time to catch my attention. I nodded and tried to focus. I knew what he and Ashcroft were thinking because I was wondering the same thing myself: How was I going to land the plane without crashing?

Soon the aerodrome came in sight and the hope of it made me more alert. Ashcroft shot ahead and zoomed low over the field, waving his wings to let the ground crew know that something was up. Then he rejoined us. We came down together, with Billy just a little ahead of me. I reduced speed. My plane listed and I forced her steady against the wind with my rudder pedals.

Dust kicked up from Billy's wheels.

"A little closer," I said to myself. "Just a little more." The ground came up quickly and I eased back the throttle. Adjusting the tail caused terrible pain: every time I pushed with my left foot against the rudder bar, it sent a shock wave through my shoulder. I landed unsteadily on one wheel and had to fight nausea to get the other wheel down. The landing wreaked havoc on my shoulder. I felt the undercarriage go.

The Strutter slid along the ground on its belly and began turning in a slow circle. A moment later it came to a stop. Someone leaned into the cockpit and switched off the throttle. I stared numbly at the control panel.

"Sir?" someone shouted. "Sir, can you hear me?"

Chapter 8
November 1916

The bullet had passed right through my shoulder. It tore through muscle but thankfully did not shatter the bone. Billy and Ashcroft stood beside the stretcher as the ground crew loaded me into a truck. My shoulder hurt so badly I felt my legs go weak. "Sorry, son," a man said as he applied a pressure bandage. "But this will keep you alive. You've lost a lot of blood and I won't let you lose a drop more."

"You'll be all right, Stitch!" Billy said.

"Good as new!" Ashcroft added.

"We'll let Nellie and your family know," Billy said. He sounded very worried.

I couldn't find my voice or even nod.

I was taken to a hospital in Ochey. They administered an injection of morphine and the pain eased considerably. Sometime later I woke up in a bed with my arm and shoulder completely immobile. My uniform was gone, replaced with a hospital gown. My arm ached dully.

For the next few days I lay in discomfort, with

the doctor checking on me every few hours. One morning a nurse peered down at me. *"Bonjour, monsieur,"* she said quietly. "You have friends to see you."

Billy and Ashcroft swept up behind the nurse, grinning like idiots. "Hurrah!" Billy trumpeted before being shushed by the nurse. They told me that I had been sleeping on and off for four days.

"Luxury!" Billy said in a loud whisper. "You sitting here with pretty nurses feeding you by hand day and night. I want to get shot too."

"You're not as good-looking as Stitch," Ashcroft countered. "You've got to shave off that moustache. Or at least half of it."

Billy wiggled his moustache at Ashcroft and said, "Hurrah."

I was so happy to see them I felt a tear squeeze out.

"None of that now, Stitch," Ashcroft said with a grin. "We don't want to make Nellie jealous."

Before I could say a word Billy held up his hand. "Yes, we wrote to your Nellie and to your parents. No pranks. Told them the whole story." There was not an ounce of humour in his voice and I knew he meant every word.

"It's coming up to Christmas before too long," Ashcroft said. "The lucky man might get to enjoy the season with mistletoe while the rest of us have the Hun as company."

Both of them looked tired. Billy's eyes were dark and his face haggard. "There's more action. We've been up a few times since your injury," he said. "They tell us a leave is coming shortly, and God knows we need it."

A couple of days later another flyer stopped by my bedside — a fellow Canadian, from British Columbia. He had sandy blond hair and a marvellous smile. He was visiting a wounded friend. "Townend, aren't you?" he asked.

I nodded.

"Raymond Collishaw." He held out his hand. "You did well up there, so they tell me," he said. "You've been given credit for taking down an Albatros." He smiled when my eyebrows went up. "And best of all, you're on leave."

"How long?" I stammered.

"Not for me to say," he responded. "Where will you go? They'll pretty much let you go where you like — if it's within reason."

"Redcar," I said without hesitating.

"I did my flight training there," he said. "It's not exactly a resort, you know."

I didn't respond.

He nodded. "Ah! A girl then, is it? Good man.

Just make sure you come back fit. We'll see you in January."

"I will!"

Two days later I was issued leave papers and was transported to England. The train stopped at Grimsby on the way to Redcar and I could not resist stepping off the train. I was due at my billet before nightfall, but with trains operating on schedule I was certain I could make it to Redcar on time, even with a short visit to Grimsby.

I bought a large box of chocolates and found a farmer in the town who was willing to take me to the Timpson farm. Nellie and I had been sending each other letters regularly. But was it enough to mean anything? I certainly knew how I felt about her. We told each other so much in our letters that I felt I knew her so well, more than our one and only visit had afforded. I could hardly contain my excitement.

The farmer let me off at the top of the Timpson lane. As I approached the farmhouse I saw a stooped figure mending a fence.

Nellie looked up. She shaded her eyes from the sun and looked at me long and hard. Then she ran. Without a word she threw her arms around me and kissed me. My doubts were gone.

Her brothers stepped onto the porch and made

their way towards us. Nellie slipped her arm around my waist to support me. The boys ran up to us like pups, yelping and asking so many questions I hardly knew where to begin.

Mr. Timpson appeared at the midday meal. He shook my good hand firmly. "Welcome, lad," he said. He glanced over my shoulder. "How is it with Mr. Miller?"

"He's well, sir," I replied. "Still flying until the end of the week. He hopes to join me at Redcar." I told the Timpsons about France and had to repeat the story of my injury three times before the boys were satisfied. On a suggestion from Nellie, I attempted to sketch the skirmish. It was a poor try, left-handed, but the boys held up the picture like a trophy. Mr. Timpson asked for details about Europe and about the progress of the war. Seems they couldn't get enough news, and sometimes had to wait until they went into town or to church. Nellie seemed as interested as he was.

"It's bad then, is it?" Mr. Timpson asked. "At the Front."

I thought of Robert's letters, of the friends he had lost. "Yes, sir," I replied. "Very bad."

He cast an eye on his eldest son. "Do they think it will last another year?"

I shook my head. "No one knows."

He nodded and said they had lost quite a few boys from the town. He changed the topic after that and asked about our farm in Winnipeg. He was pleased with my knowledge of farming and curious about some of the techniques we used in Canada.

As the afternoon lengthened I glanced out the window.

"I'll need to go soon," I said with regret.

Mr. Timpson took me to the station on their wagon and once again Nellie was allowed to come. This time the three of us shared a blanket. Nellie slipped me her hand and I held on tight. She gave me a hug when we reached Grimsby Station and whispered, "I'll find a reason to come to Redcar."

Arrangements had been made for me to billet with the Baxters, a family who lived near the centre of town. The home was small but cozy, and Mrs. Baxter fussed over me as if she were my own mother. Once a day I went to the base hospital, where they changed the dressings on my wound. I refused further morphine injections, based on warnings I'd received from a pilot back at Ochey. It was easy to become addicted to such a strong drug, and some of the men had fallen prey to it.

On the fourth day of my stay at Redcar there was a knock at the front entrance. I could hear

Mrs. Baxter exchange pleasantries and then open the door wider. A soldier entered and removed his hat. "Paul," he said quietly.

I stared hard and then gasped. "Robert!"

I hardly recognized him. His face was gaunt and he looked 10 years older than when I had last seen him. He moved stiffly, like an old man. But more than anything, his eyes looked drained of life. I was shocked to see him in such a state.

Mrs. Baxter came to our rescue. "To the fireside — both of you!" she commanded. "We'll all catch our death of cold standing here. Leave your bag, lad. I'll see that it gets to your room. You'll stay with us."

Despite Robert's condition, it was a joyous reunion, and in minutes we were sitting by the fire, sipping tea and downing Mrs. Baxter's cookies as fast as she brought them. We launched into stories of our farm and I laughed as I had not done in months. "How did you know where to find me?" I asked.

"Your buddy Billy sent me a letter. Could have bowled me over, I got it so fast. I was due for leave, decided to chase you down, and here I am."

"I've missed you, Robert," I said with a sigh. "And there's times I can hardly wait to see home."

"Home," he said, as if tasting the word. He

smiled again weakly. Then he stared at the fire and fell silent. I waited. For a moment I thought he had fallen asleep. Finally he said, "It's bad, Paul. Bad beyond words. I'm going to get it soon enough."

"Don't talk like that, Robert," I said, but he held up his hand to stop me.

"The things I say to you, I cannot tell Mom and Dad or Sarah. You've been in battle, so you can understand." Then he spoke of the giant guns incessantly firing and blowing holes in the ground and in the men all around him. He described charges over ground littered with bodies. He described men acting like animals. And he told me about the trenches — diseases, rats the size of cats biting in the night, the sounds of men dying, the awful stench. He spoke for a long time and then fell silent again to stare at the fire.

"Robert," I said, "at least you're still alive."

He looked at me through tired eyes. "Sometimes I'm not sure. There so much death, I can't always tell."

That night Robert screamed as I have never heard a man scream before. I leapt from my bed and ran to his room.

"Robert!" I cried. "What's wrong?" He mumbled incoherently. After a moment Mrs. Baxter appeared in the doorway carrying a candle. Robert stared up at us with wild, terrified eyes. "I'll make tea," Mrs. Baxter said simply, as if she had witnessed this sort of thing before. She handed me another candle. Robert was soaked in sweat and gasping. He gripped my arm with tremendous strength. "It's all right," he said, catching his breath. "It will pass. Let's go sit by the fire."

We went downstairs and I stirred up the coals in the fireplace. Mrs. Baxter brought us tea and then headed off for bed. I told Robert about the Curtiss Aviation School, about coming to Redcar and meeting Nellie. He listened attentively and calmed himself in the warmth of the fire and the tea.

"I'd like to meet Nellie," he said. "Thinking of you and a lovely girl sounds so . . . " He paused and then said, "Hopeful."

"What happened up there?" I asked, pointing to the bedrooms.

"Horrible dreams," he murmured. "They come every night that I'm not in the trenches." He looked up from his tea. "Tell me more about Nellie."

In the morning I found Robert in the kitchen, helping Mrs. Baxter make breakfast. The wildness was gone from his eyes and he smiled more frequently. When he left the kitchen to put food on the table, Mrs. Baxter whispered, "Anyone who's been in the trenches screams at night. At least, that's been our experience. It ain't natural, what's happening to the boys over there, God help them."

When the post arrived I received the best news. "Nellie's coming tomorrow morning," I exclaimed. "She's delivering some socks to the base. We can meet her at the station!"

Robert went with me to the hospital after breakfast and stood by while the doctor re-bandaged my wound. "It's healing well," he said. "There's no infection."

It turned out that Robert was being treated for trench foot, a condition caused by standing for long periods of time in the cold, water-filled and filthy trenches. "She works hard, your Nellie," Robert said a few minutes later. "And she cares for you. That much is clear."

We met Nellie at the station the next day. She looked smashing. I hardly recognized the farm girl I'd seen a few days before. She linked arms with Robert and me and our day began. Robert raised his eyebrows at me and winked. His first impression was a good one.

"We shall take a tour of the quaint town of Red-car," Nellie announced. We stopped at all the shops, looking in the windows or going inside. Nellie's wit and humour did wonders for Robert. "This — " she pronounced dramatically at one window " — is a bake shop. I am sure you do not have such a fancy thing in Canada, being the colony and all."

"No, your ladyship," Robert quipped. "But we're improving every year."

"I'm sure you're trying," she answered.

While she was busy buying cookies for us, Robert leaned over to me. "She's wonderful, Paul. She makes me feel as if there isn't a war."

I let the two of them do most of the talking. Nellie told Robert about my landing in the Timpson field. Robert told story after story about our farm and family. I got the sense that they were interviewing each other, teasing out information. Their comments, while often funny, were supplying answers to topics that Nellie and I had not had the chance to discuss. I smiled. I could not have asked for two better people to be on my side.

When it was time to take her back to the station, Nellie held on to me for a long time. "Your brother has been hurt," she whispered in my ear. "In his heart and mind and body. But he seems a good man."

"Did you have a good time?" I asked her.

"Better than good. I just wish we had longer . . . and a little time alone."

At supper that night, Robert suddenly stopped

eating and pointed his fork at me. "Marry her, Paul! Marry Nellie."

I choked on a piece of shepherd's pie. "I'm *nineteen*," I stammered. "And she's even younger."

With his fork still pointed at me he answered, "After all we've been through, how old do you have to be to get married?"

Chapter 9
January 1917

I returned to France in the new year, only to discover that many of us were being transferred to the more forward position of Vert Galand. Most of the British officers in the huts around us were in 55 Squadron.

Billy and Ashcroft fairly tackled me when I arrived.

"Good old Stitch!" Billy shouted as I jumped down from the transport truck.

I stared at him more closely and noticed even deeper lines in his face than had been there last time I'd seen him. Both he and Ashcroft looked haggard. "Didn't you get leave?" I asked.

Ashcroft shouldered my bag as we made for our hut. "Sure we did," he said. "We got four days after you left and then another four at Christmas." So they had seen a lot of action while I was away. No wonder they looked so haggard. It certainly gave me a sense of what to expect at Vert Galand. As if on cue, I noticed the dull pounding of artillery. It was not far — much closer than at Ochey.

As we walked to the aerodrome I glanced at the airstrip. "Where are the Strutters?" I asked. "And what are these?" Four planes, the likes of which I had never seen, were sitting side by side in the field. They were sleek machines, more so than the Strutters, and the fuselage was pleasantly rounded.

"Sopwith Pup," said Ashcroft. "They're faster than the Strutters. Billy's taken it to a hundred and three miles per hour!"

"And I'll get it to a hundred and six soon," Billy boasted.

Ashcroft jogged over the thin layer of snow to one of the aircraft and patted the cockpit. "This little pup has a ceiling of almost eighteen thousand feet!" I shook my head in wonder. That was considerably higher than the Strutter.

"She handles beautifully," Ashcroft added, his breath puffing out clouds in the freezing air. "Playful as a sparrow. Fast, and she can hold her altitude."

I pointed to the four painted marks below the cockpit.

"Ashcroft's count is four," Billy said. "Two in one day! We had five Albatros scouts on the run. Ashy here lured them right across our lines, and between us and the anti-aircraft crew, only one Hun went home!" He dramatized firing a machine gun and then his hand became a plane spiralling to the ground. Ashcroft laughed.

Their grisly enthusiasm was startling. I had felt anger in the heat of battle before, even the exhilarating terror of the chase, but there was something chilling about the way Billy and Ashcroft spoke.

It was bitterly cold the next morning too. The clouds were low and by 10:00 a.m. we were given word that there would be no flying. Instead, we were to help sandbag the huts, the anti-aircraft guns and the hangar. Our last home at Ochey had taken terrible hits from German raids in December, losing many of their planes, as well as all the windows in their huts.

The British officers from 55 Squadron were upset about having to do manual labour, especially filling the bags with sand. "They didn't sign up for this sort of thing, don't you know, old chap," quipped Ashcroft as he passed another bag on to me. I grinned and pushed the bag into place against the wall of the hangar. It was as close to farm work as we had experienced so far and I found it refreshing, despite the ache from my wound.

Billy and I decided to finish sandbagging our own hut, even if he was the one who'd be doing most of the lifting. It was merciless work in the afternoon chill, but news of the Ochey bombings was fresh in our minds. Ashcroft joined us for the last half hour and we finished the job. It was none too soon. The Germans attacked Vert Galand the next morning.

Our anti-aircraft guns started firing even before the air-raid sirens went off. The explosions were so loud I thought a bomb had landed in our hut. I was thrown out of my bed and crashed onto the floor. The ground shook violently and it was impossible to stand up. I clung to a bed frame to keep from sprawling on my back. One of the oil lanterns sailed over our heads and across the room. Billy shouted something unintelligible. A window burst. I ducked as glass shot across the floor. Explosion followed explosion as I held on tight to my bed.

There was a brief lull. Then machine guns began strafing the nearby huts.

"Get down, Billy!" I shouted, scrambling under the bed. He landed with his head next to mine. Seconds later, bullets tore through the roof of our hut and shattered our remaining window.

After a minute or so the bombs stopped, but the anti-aircraft guns continued as we pulled on our boots and ran outside. Massive craters dotted our landing field. Two Sopwith Pups burned like torches. The hangar was still intact, thanks to our sandbagging. When I turned around to look at our hut, I gasped. A chunk of metal the size of my fist was embedded in one of the sandbags near the door. I shook my head. Without the protection we'd laid down the day before, the shrapnel would have gone right through the wall.

When all were accounted for, two people were dead — a mechanic and a nurse. The mechanic had been hit by shrapnel. The poor nurse had just come off shift and could not find cover when the planes flew over. She'd been killed by bullets, not a bomb. Someone had shot her down as she ran.

I was so angry my voice shook. "Let's go," I said to Ashcroft and Billy. "Let's go *now*. We can catch them."

"Easy, Stitch," said Billy.

He helped lift the nurse onto a stretcher and then turned to me. Lowering his voice, he said, "We shot up their hospital a few days after Christmas."

"What?" I asked.

Ashcroft moved closer so as not to be over-heard. "There was smoke everywhere, Stitch. I swear to God, we couldn't see what we were doing. There was no cross on the building — at least, nothing visible to us. When fifty bombs go off and you're dodging anti-aircraft bullets, you can't see everything. I shot at every building in sight."

Billy kicked at the smoking ground. "The commander received a wire from the Hun the next day. We were as shocked as he was."

I put my face in my hands. No wonder the Germans had attacked like this. Why was it all so complicated? The nurse looked hardly older than Nellie.

Billy put his hand on my shoulder. "Steady now, Stitch, steady. We've got some fires to put out. Then we'll go get them. And we'll get them back twice over."

We were told to stand ready for 8:00 a.m. Billy, Ashcroft and I sipped coffee and waited in the dark. I was nervous. It had been some time since I'd last flown, and once again I'd be in a new plane. Even with my friends' assurances that the Pup was brilliant, I couldn't be certain until I had taken her up myself.

Ashcroft stamped out a cigarette and looked up at me in the glowing light of our wood stove. "Keep a wary eye out for Jasta 11, Stitch, my boy."

"Why?"

"They've got a pilot — the Red Baron, they call him. Real name is von Richthofen. He flies an Albatros D.II. He's crazy. Not even the best pilot

I've seen, but he's fearless and sly as a fox. Flies with his brother, they say."

"They all fly with their relatives!" Billy grunted. "They're royalty, these Huns. Not farm boys like us."

"And they've taken to flying out of the sun. They perch up high on patrol and then fly out into your blind spot, with the sun making them practically invisible," said Ashcroft.

"The good thing," Billy said with a wry smile, "is that there's so much rain pouring down over this godforsaken war that poor old Jasta 11 can't use the sun very often."

"And another thing, Stitch," Ashcroft said, ignoring Billy. "They call themselves the Flying Circus — whole groups of planes attacking at once rather than in twos and threes."

It was a curious name. I tried to picture what it might look like in the sky.

The patrol was called to take off and I found myself sitting in the cockpit of the beautiful and mysterious Sopwith Pup. Billy and Ashcroft were right. The controls were marvellous. Takeoff was smooth. I'd worried needlessly — all my skills returned in an instant. The one disconcerting thing was that my hand started shaking again. I had forgotten about it in Redcar. And now it was back. I wondered if Robert was screaming again at night.

Dawn broke in the east, showing gathering clouds and the threat of more precipitation. There were five of us in single-seat Sopwith Pups. I grinned under my face covering. What a sight we must have been in these sleek new planes. If only Nellie could have seen us!

We flew in a tight formation and I could tell by each pilot's focus that flying so close to the Western Front was a serious thing. From the corners of my eyes I watched my friends performing rituals: tightening chinstraps or making the sign of the cross. Billy kept patting the side of his Pup as if he were reassuring a nervous horse. We maintained a low altitude for over a mile and I saw more clearly than ever before what Robert's world looked like.

The early light revealed a terrible scene. From the sky it looked as if the earth had been emptied of all living things. Pockmarks covered the ground like a thousand mud stains on a white blanket. Trenches zigzagged across the land as far as the eye could see. Ruined guns and armaments lay broken where they had been struck. There were bodies too. Far too many.

I shuddered as I stared at Robert's world. Little wonder he had nightmares. And little wonder if he questioned his chances for survival. Who could live in such a desolate place? I remembered what Robert had said about pilots and planes, but there was no doubt in my mind that the men on the ground faced a grimmer challenge.

We stayed close to our own lines, travelling the length of the trenches and venturing only a short way into No Man's Land. The trenches were separated by only 300 yards in some places, and there was danger of being shot at from the ground. It was light enough now that I could see our men hunched in their trenches. One man raised his canteen to us in salute.

I played with the wind a little and fluttered from side to side to feel the Pup's agility in the air. It was a marvellous machine and it felt good to focus on flying rather than the horrors below.

Ashcroft suddenly waved and caught our attention. He pointed ahead and then signalled "five" with his hand. Billy waved back and nodded his acknowledgement. It took a moment for me to find the enemy planes. They were still behind our lines and making for No Man's Land. If we were lucky, they'd be low on fuel.

Billy banked sharply to intercept. My admiration for our new planes increased as we followed, gaining elevation faster than in our old Strutters.

The Germans spotted us and started climbing. They were no match for the Pups, however, and we remained above them in our race for the height advantage.

We engaged in battle directly above our trenches. What a show it must have been for those on the ground: five against five, our Pups against two Albatros D.IIs and three Halberstadt D.IIs. For a moment I wondered if the Red Baron was among them, but as the first enemy flew by I saw from their markings that they were not from Jasta 11. Regardless of their leader, they were good pilots.

Ashcroft was hit immediately. Smoke billowed from his fuselage and he disengaged from the fight. I was relieved to see him still looking about. At least he was alive! And then I was caught up in fighting for my life and lost sight of him. An Albatros came up from below and I flitted to the side, exactly as I'd been practising en route. I dodged it and then opened fire as it went past me. The bullets traced along the cockpit and the pilot suddenly slumped forward. It happened so quickly I was stunned to see the plane spiral downward, a stream of smoke pouring from the engine. Seconds later there was an explosion and the plane burst into fire in the sky.

"Got him!" I shouted. There was no time to

think about the hit, for a Halberstadt roared right above my top wing. I followed it for a moment but it was moving too quickly for me to catch up. I searched all around, seeking my next quarry.

Everywhere I looked, planes dove and looped, guns chattered in wild acrobatics. The Germans had named their Flying Circus well. While their planes were faster and better armed, our Pups were gloriously agile. I dropped in behind a Halberstadt and fired a burst. The bullets sped into empty space below its undercarriage. The pilot kept adjusting his altitude and shifting from side to side. I followed closely, firing a burst whenever his tail came into my gun sights.

The Albatros suddenly banked and put on a burst of speed. Although I could not keep up with it, my Pup turned so smoothly that it reappeared in my sights. I fired yet another burst and then prepared to shoot again.

At first it looked as if nothing had happened. I could see the pilot trying to adjust something in the cockpit, likely his throttle, when his engine spouted a plume of smoke. I gave a whoop when its nose turned towards the ground. The pilot had painted a skull and crossbones near the cockpit and I made a mental note so I could identify him later in my logbook. It looked as if he were going to crash on our side and our soldiers would find him first. He worked his flaps well, and if he was worth anything as a pilot he would escape without serious injury.

When I banked around again, the remaining two Albatroses and the Halberstadts were racing through No Man's Land towards Germany. No doubt they were low on fuel and could not risk another minute of fighting. As we re-formed I tried to get a glimpse of Ashcroft. I scanned below for any sign of him, but all I could see was the pockmarked earth and tiny bands of men racing like ants across the surface. We descended low along the ground a few hundred yards behind our lines, searching for him. Nothing. Billy took us home.

"Ashcroft was alive," I said once we were on the ground. "I saw his head moving, looking about." We walked towards the hangar. I couldn't help but think of poor Williams, who had crashed into a tree after surviving a fight.

The same thought must have occurred to Billy, for he kept pressing the other pilots for information. "Did anyone see where he went down?" Billy asked.

"No Man's Land, for sure," someone said. "He was headed beyond our lines, trying to keep his nose up."

Billy and I glanced at each other. There could

be several reasons for that. His control stick might have been damaged by a bullet, but at least his ailerons were still working — they would keep his nose up. If he was injured himself then there was no telling what he could or could not do. I held on to the image in my mind of his head moving and looking about — alive when I last saw him.

It was so difficult to write a flight report with Ashcroft still missing. I kept turning around, expecting him to walk in and say something funny. One of the men clapped my shoulder and said I would win a medal for knocking out two planes in a single mission. Ashcroft's absence kept me from celebration. I wrote as clearly as I could, noting the markings on the Albatros and Halberstadt as I had seen them.

When we got into our hut I sat on my bed and said a prayer aloud for Ashcroft. Billy removed his hat and whispered, "I hope to God he's all right."

* * *

Just before midnight the door to our hut opened and a figure crossed the room to stand next to the stove.

"Billy?" I asked, half asleep.

"Hello, Stitch!" called a cheerful voice.

"Ashcroft!" I leapt out of bed and tackled him. Billy joined me and the three of us threw our arms around one another and bounced around in circles as if we were schoolboys. Ashcroft had a cut on his cheek, already stitched, and a black eye. Otherwise, he looked none the worse for wear.

"God save the Aussies!" he said. "Two of them pulled me from my plane in No Man's Land. We scurried back to our lines with the Hun firing all around us."

It wasn't long before more of us were gathered around and Ashcroft told his story three more times in detail. It was a close shave to say the least.

Bullets had ripped through his fuel line and he lost power. He thought he was a dead man when smoke appeared near the propeller, but the damage was only superficial. The flames went out rather quickly and beyond all luck he managed to keep his nose up. He crash-landed in No Man's Land, bounced twice and lost his landing gear after the second strike. He ended up in an enormous crater with his Pup upside down. Dazed for some time, likely several minutes, he managed to remove his safety belt and fall out of the plane. He was too stunned to move and simply lay in the crater for a long while.

"I could hear a scurrying sound and I thought a troop of trench rats was on its way to chew on my shoes," he said with a grin. "But it was our lads — Australians, actually — who crept into No Man's Land to get me out." He wiped a hand across his forehead and then continued. "There was a great deal of shooting. I guess the Hun sent scouts in as well. I kept my head down. Next thing I knew, someone hauled me to my feet. Then we ran, zigzagging through a maze of craters for cover, bullets striking the ground at our feet and whining over our heads. We scrambled back across our lines. I hopped into a truck and they brought me back here. They were brave lads, those Aussies. I owe them my life."

We stood quietly for a moment until Billy shouted, "A toast! A toast to Ashcroft and his return!"

As we raised our glasses Ashcroft added, "And to the Aussies, who know the meaning of courage."

Chapter 10
February 1917

We flew almost daily during that long stretch of dark and freezing days. I had never been so tired or exhilarated in my life. Coffee was now a staple for me, morning, noon and night. For Father's sake I left alcohol alone. Billy and Ashcroft, however, were awash every other day. The pressure and strain on our emotions was severe, especially after near-death experiences, and it was hard to blame anyone for taking to drink. But there were consequences. Twice Billy stumbled out to the airstrip at dawn after a hard night's drinking. If I hadn't stopped him he would have started drinking again before climbing into his plane.

"You're still drunk!" I snapped at him one day as his propeller started up.

He looked at me indignantly and said, "I like shooting at . . . " he struggled over the word *Albatros* before waving his hand dismissively at the air and adding, " . . . *them* when I'm drunk." He tapped my chest as I stood on the step of his Pup. "In fact, I'm a better shot drunk than you are sober." I jumped down and ran for my plane. If I didn't hurry, the fool would try to take on Jasta 11 on his own.

The ground crew had my plane readied and we had only started the prop when Billy roared past us on his way into the sky. It was the worst takeoff I'd seen in days.

One of the crew raised his eyebrows at me. "I know, I know," I shouted. "He's an idiot. I'll catch him up." The man said nothing in return and saluted me as I pulled away from the blocks. There were two other pilots on the sortie, Rogers and Bunyan, both Canadian. They knew Billy well enough to realize what had happened. Both hurried to join me.

Billy was flying at a ridiculous speed. It took me 10 minutes to catch up to him. The other two were well behind us. I scanned the skies. All clear. The artillery boomed below and I shook my head in wonder that Billy had the sense to keep high, out of the range of the anti-aircraft fire. As he neared our lines and No Man's Land, I pulled even with him. His protective mask was off. He made several unsuccessful attempts to button it into place.

Bunyan caught up to us on the opposite side of Billy and drew even closer for a better look. Rogers flew a hundred feet above, keeping watch for the enemy. When Billy threw his hands up helplessly at his flapping mask, Bunyan yelled and shook his fist at Billy. Then he pointed to the earth below. Billy shook his head, *No*. This time Bunyan let go of his controls and made a gesture of throttling Billy. Again he pointed down. Finally Billy pulled out and headed back.

Bunyan landed first and was already marching across the field when Billy came down. He botched the landing but still managed to hold it together without losing his undercarriage. Bunyan stood below Billy's cockpit and told him to come down. Billy got out slowly. When his feet touched the ground, Bunyan grabbed him by the coat and hauled him off at a jog towards the huts. I made to follow but Rogers caught hold of my jacket.

"Easy, Stitch. It will only be what's good for him. No real harm."

The two men disappeared behind Hut 4. The ground crew could hardly concentrate on the planes, they were so intrigued by what was going on. Rogers smoked a cigarette and we stood without speaking for several minutes.

Bunyan and Billy came back shortly. Their helmets were off, as were their gloves, and both looked dishevelled. Billy's nose was bleeding. Bunyan looked as if he had taken a hit to the eye. Rogers stamped out his cigarette.

"Looks as though they came out about even," he said. "Billy's made of tough stuff. I wouldn't last a round with Bunyan."

As they neared us, Bunyan threw his arm around Billy's shoulder and they shook hands.

The incident was not reported. In my logbook I wrote: *Pilot ill, forced to return 3 miles out.* The others wrote the same.

Billy sustained mild frostbite to his chin. The doctor told him that if he had been out any longer, he would have lost a good 5 inches of his face. Billy stopped drinking for several days after that. When he did drink again, he covered the top of his glass just as Ashcroft tried to pour a fourth drink.

"No, no, Ash," Billy said. "I don't want to make Bunyan look like a little girl again." Aside to me, he added, "If I hadn't got my hand up in time he'd have broken my nose." He twirled his moustache and said quietly, "Hurrah."

* * *

A week later three of us went up for dawn patrol. Word of a Hun raid for that morning had been reported the night before and the commander wanted regular patrols even with the foul weather. We were flying so often now that it didn't seem to matter if the Germans were planning a raid or not; we were either countering or attacking, day after day.

Ashcroft took the lead while Bunyan and I flew off his wing in V-formation. The ceiling was low and we found clear skies at 8000 feet. We also found seven German fighters passing through the same space. Bursting through the clouds, we surprised the Germans as much as their presence surprised us. The moment we saw them, Ashcroft flicked his wings. It was a reflex, a split-second hesitation, as if considering retreat. And then it was gone and he held steady, committing us to the fight.

My blood began to pound and my right hand shook. I glanced at Bunyan. He nodded but gave no signal of his intentions or plans as to how we might fight this battle. If we had one more plane with us we could have broken off in pairs, one to attack and one to defend. But as we'd left the aerodrome, Rogers's engine had malfunctioned and Ashcroft took us up without him. I was still wondering how we would handle seven planes when Ashcroft signalled to us. Bunyan and I increased throttle and tightened formation.

Twenty seconds later the Hun was upon us. The lead plane had a distinctive colour — bright red. Two planes on the outside of their formation broke away from the others, but I lost sight of them as we engaged the first wave of fighters. Ashcroft banked sharply to port and I followed. Bunyan disappeared below me in an attempt to escape an onslaught from the flank. I managed to stay close to Ashcroft and give him cover, holding off an Albatros on his left flank with a burst of fire. A flash of red paint passed between the sights of my guns and then disappeared.

As we came around in the turn we were beset by attackers from below and above. I understood more than ever what these German flyers meant by calling themselves the Flying Circus. They were everywhere in the sky and flying new machines, Albatros D.IIIs, which could climb quickly and high.

Fear was lost to concentration. Sweat poured down the sides of my face. An Albatros suddenly came up in front of me in order to escape Ashcroft's onslaught. The Hun banked to port, a classic manoeuvre, in order to expose me to his gunner. Instinctively I banked starboard. As the distance grew between us, I came back over and reduced speed, falling right in behind and slightly below him. The gunner couldn't reach me without blowing off his own tail.

Before I could fire, there was a sudden loss of

power and I wrestled with the ailerons to keep the Pup from going down nose first. The prop sputtered several times and my stomach dropped. Smoke erupted from the fuselage.

Ashcroft and Bunyan were nowhere to be seen as the fighting continued in circles above. Far more alarming, however, was the looming presence of the Albatros that stayed with me. He remained on my tail as I descended. I hunched my shoulders and waited for bullets to rip into my back. When the pilot didn't fire, I turned to look at him. He eyed the skies around him and then suddenly increased throttle and made to pass me.

As he pulled even he did not pass, but matched my speed, our planes wingtip to wingtip. We stared at one another for a moment, the clouds of smoke from my engine obscuring the view every few seconds. I couldn't see his face very well, for he was as covered up against the elements as I was. But there was a determination in his gestures, in his presence, that caught my attention. It was then that I noticed the red paint on his fuselage.

My propeller stopped again at that moment and did not restart. I looked one last time at the pilot beside me. He nodded, saluted and then veered off sharply as my plane plummeted towards the earth. Without the engine to provide power, I felt the buffeting wind all the more severely. Running properly, the Pup was a flitting sparrow, but without power, she kept wanting to flip and spiral. At least my engine was no longer smoking. The clouds hid the ground below and I could only hope I was not headed for trees or a hilltop. It was difficult to know if I was gliding towards friendly territory or not, as my attention had been taken with the fighting. The smoke, at least, had lessened greatly.

When I hit the low ceiling of clouds, the Pup jumped and bounced in the turbulence. Again the nose wanted to go down. "Come on, Pup," I shouted. "Get your nose up! Up, up, up!" At about 1000 feet the clouds cleared enough for me to see something of the ground. It was all trees. At the same moment, out of sheer desperation, I tried the starter again. To my shock, the engine turned. I pulled back on the stick and gained some altitude. Several minutes later, I levelled off. Not knowing if my engine would conk out again, I made straight for base, thankful to be alive and with a good story to tell Billy.

Chapter 11
February–March 1917

When I returned to base, I learned that Bunyan was dead. According to the ground crew, he was found shot through the head — dead before his plane crashed.

After my plane went down, Jasta 11 had pursued Ashcroft and Bunyan without mercy. Ashcroft was struck once in the chest and once in the foot. He lost consciousness and plummeted to the earth. The Hun let him go, assuming he was dead. Ashcroft revived, however, and pulled out from the dive. He miraculously landed his plane and was taken to the field hospital at the base. When I saw him the next morning, the doctor had just removed the bullet from his chest.

Billy came in and gave me a bear hug. "I knew it!" he said. "I just knew it. Stitch has a guardian angel who won't let us down so easily." He sobered when he saw me looking at Ashcroft. "He's done," Billy said quietly. "I don't mean he's dying. No, not him. But he's through with this war." He lifted the blanket at the bottom of the bed. Ashcroft's right foot was missing. "It was smashed beyond repair," Billy murmured.

It was a terrible shock to see our friend so damaged. "Does he know?" I whispered.

Billy shook his head. "Hasn't woken up since they brought him in. That's not a good sign, but the doctor said he could easily have struck his head on the landing. He definitely has a concussion. So that's likely it. Right now he's sleeping."

In our hut that night Billy looked up from his drink quite suddenly and said, "How many Hun do you think I could kill at one go?"

I stared blankly for a moment.

"How many can I kill?" he added. "Before they get me."

"I don't know."

"I want to get five of them for killing Bunyan and five more for taking away Ashcroft," he said. "Do you think that is reasonable?"

When I didn't answer he started to say something else, but caught himself when his voice cracked. It unnerved me to see him like this. With a half sob he added, "I *hate* them, Stitch! I hate all the Hun. I want them dead. Damn them for this filthy war. They killed my brother and now they're killing my friends."

I walked over to our tiny table. I took Ashcroft's

cup and my own and poured a little rum. Then I walked over to Billy. He looked up at me, eyes wide. "But you don't drink, Stitch."

"No, I don't. I do this for Ashcroft and for you. This once only." I raised our injured friend's cup. "And we will drink a toast to Bunyan — but only one toast because we know how he felt about pilots and drinking."

Billy absently rubbed his nose. "Yes, we know how he felt about that."

"To Ashcroft. And to Bunyan. Sunny skies ahead."

"To Ashcroft and Bunyan."

The rum burned my throat all the way down, and I spluttered and coughed up half of it onto the floor. Billy laughed and thumped my back. "Good old Stitch. You'd better stay with tea. We said we'd stick together, didn't we?" he said, giving my arm a punch. "We'll take the Hun down together."

His words suddenly evoked a memory. "I saw him!" I exclaimed.

He looked at me quizzically.

"The Red Baron," I said. "I saw him. He was the one that sent me crashing."

"Really?"

"Yes! He conked out my engine and then flew beside me while I struggled to keep the Pup in the air. He could have finished me easily. Instead, he waited until my propeller stopped and then pulled away as I went down. It was uncanny."

Billy took a last swig. "I hope I meet him," he said. "And I hope I get the chance to watch his red plane fall from the sky."

* * *

For the next several weeks we flew at a reckless pace. Billy lost a great deal of weight and his face became gaunt. When I stole a glance at the mirror I was astonished at the change in my own appearance. There were black patches under my eyes and a bald spot on the back of my head. The doctor said that the hair loss was due to stress and that it would grow back. As much as I missed Nellie, I was glad she couldn't see me looking so ragged.

We had continued sending letters and there was not a hint of her losing her affection. To my great delight a letter also arrived from Sarah, who reported that all was well at home. My mother had caught a terrible fever but had recovered sufficiently. Sarah had received a letter from Robert. His trench foot problem had flared up again and was causing a great deal of discomfort, and for some reason he appeared more susceptible to it than others. I remembered the horrible condition of his feet. On the positive side, it meant that he had been out of action for the past three weeks and hence out of the line of fire.

At the bottom of her letter Sarah noted something else that sent my heart soaring.

Your Nellie and I have exchanged letters and become friends. So you have but two choices: Come and fly me to England, or bring her home with you.

"Do I get to be best man?" Billy quipped when I showed him the letter.

"Of course. I mean, if we . . . I . . . " My face flushed and Billy burst out laughing. It was one of the only pleasant highlights of early March.

Word also reached us about Raymond Collishaw, the pilot from British Columbia who had paid me a visit after my injury. He was part of Black Flight now, a Canadian wing that was taking German planes down at such a shocking rate it was gaining quite a reputation. If I'd known he was such an ace, I'd have given his hand a longer shake. He seemed like a very decent sort of person.

* * *

A few days later we were sent up with a larger force than usual. It was common for us to fly in twos and threes and it was certainly not unknown for a lone plane to go up for patrol. On that day, however, twelve of us were sent up. It was a strange, exhilarating feeling to be part of such a group. We seemed to fill the air, an invincible wall of fighters. I wondered why we didn't fly like this more often.

Ashcroft had told me months previously that the Brits were cocky flyers. "A bunch of brave lunatics," he said. "And yet so bloody practical too. Their superiors are of the belief that it's better to send up only a few pilots at a time so we can only lose that many. Not like the Hun. They travel in their circuses and stick together."

We gained altitude to 8000 feet and then sorted out our formation. Billy and Rogers were on my flanks. It was strange not to have Ashcroft somewhere near, especially with so many of us flying. He was in England waiting for medical transport back to Canada. We promised to catch up when we all returned. Toronto, Ashcroft's hometown, did not seem so far now that I had been overseas. His last words to me were, "Take care of Billy. He's a wild one."

Leadership was a curious thing when it came to air combat, and I felt it distinctly on that day in March. We had lost so many pilots to the enemy and to landing accidents that it took a relatively short time to be called a veteran. New lads arrived monthly, many of them looking as if they were hardly a day past eighteen. It was Billy who reminded me that I was not that much older than some of them. With all that had happened since I left our Winnipeg farm, it was difficult to imagine that so little time had passed.

As we pressed into No Man's Land with our large formation, Rogers suddenly waved and pointed. Ahead of us and coming from the German lines were five enemy fighters, three of them Albatroses. We changed direction and moved towards them, although not so much to intercept as to observe. They were flying some 200 feet below. I waited for our leader to signal attack, but he seemed content to keep an eye on the enemy while still hunting for signs of movement on the ground. The Germans could not have missed us, and yet they did not turn away.

The sun broke from a cloud, ever so briefly, and in that instant the red fuselage of an Albatros, flying at the centre of the formation, was illuminated. Billy saw it at once and broke away from my wing.

"Idiot!" I hollered. I felt a shiver go down my spine when the red plane also pulled away from its formation. Soon the two of them were matching altitude and on a collision course.

I followed Billy, as did Rogers, and opened the

throttle in order to catch him. The wind didn't help and I felt the tug and pull on my wings, pushing us towards enemy lines. I wished for the hundredth time that Bunyan was on hand to reel Billy back in.

As our planes drew closer, Billy opened fire and white smoke trails spun out from his gun. The Baron did not fire.

Rogers took position above to act as lookout and I followed Billy in for the attack. At 100 yards Billy stopped firing, and I realized with a sinking heart that his gun had jammed. I could see him madly trying to clear the blockage. He was an easy target. At 50 yards the Baron opened fire. I heard the chatter of gunfire and then several gashes appeared in the canvas of Billy's wing. I had seen wings shorn off by bullets before, and I certainly wasn't going to let that happen to my friend.

I cleared Billy's tail and then fired several rounds. The incendiary bullets flared as they left my gun and the pilot fluttered his wings in an attempt to avoid them. Then we all roared past one another and began to turn about like knights in a jousting tournament. In that brief moment I recognized the plane and pilot that had shot me down only a short time before. No wonder the commander had sent us all up. He was tired of the Baron shooting our boys down.

We hit a large bank of cloud and I kept my turn steady, trusting Billy to do the same and lessen the risk of collision. I caught a glimpse of him. His wing appeared to be holding up in the turn. The ground was visible between patches of cloud. A swath of green caught my attention. We were drifting away from the Front and towards Germany.

We came around to find our formation broken up and a full fight in progress. Billy's gun was working again and he opened fire the moment we straightened out. There was no knowing if he was actually doing any damage, but his gun blasted away nonetheless. It jammed again a few seconds later. It did not matter. The German plane had slowed, a thin strip of white smoke erupting from its engine.

"Fuel's leaking!" I shouted. "It's going to blow! The Baron's plane is going to blow!" The thin white smoke was the first indicator that a plane's fuel tank had been pierced and was about to explode. The question was how much fuel was pouring in around his feet and how long it took for a spark or the heat of the engine to ignite the benzine. Billy started firing but his gun jammed yet again. When was he going to learn? He was so wild with hate that he was not concentrating.

The Albatros's propeller suddenly stopped and the Baron headed towards the earth. I couldn't believe it was happening, for Billy's gun had jammed three times and I'd only managed one brief burst, without a clear view.

A bright object caught my peripheral vision and I turned to see a fireball falling through the sky. It shot past the damaged Albatros some 200 yards away. The pilot looked up just as the fiery wreckage passed him, and raised his hands in triumph. The burning plane was a Sopwith Pup. Already it was completely engulfed in flames. A second later another plane, an Albatros this time, went down, streaming smoke.

I watched the Baron for close to a minute. There was no question that he was going down. I kept waiting for his plane to explode. It didn't. Billy pulled even with me and shrugged. He motioned as if to follow, but I shook my head vigorously. How ironic that only weeks ago this same enemy had watched my own plane fail and fall from the sky. He could have finished me off for certain. It was almost as if he wanted to let Providence choose for him. And perhaps Providence had, for in that moment I made the choice not to pursue the failing plane.

I pointed to the battle above us and signalled for us to join them. Billy turned frequently in his seat to look down after the Baron. After a moment he nodded and reluctantly closed in behind me. Even as we approached the remnants of the fray, the last three Germans turned away and headed across their lines. I could hear the anti-aircraft guns starting up from below. We were still out of range and none of us wanted to fly into that barrage for the sake of three planes, especially when we were such a large contingent. The risk far outweighed the benefits.

Rogers gave me a thumbs-up as we re-formed. I scanned the planes to see who was missing. Everyone I knew was still present, so it was clearly one of the new lads who had gone down. A couple of them had minimal flying experience — surrounded by experienced fighters, there was a danger of them losing concentration or being cocky.

It was life-threatening to take any of the Jasta squadrons for granted. They had pilots like Richthofen — the Red Baron of Jasta 11 — plus Ernst Udet of Jasta 15 and Werner Voss of Jasta 2. These were men worthy of respect and careful attention. We knew their names, sometimes their planes, and always their reputations. An inexperienced pilot could easily think that ten of us against one was an obvious win. Those of us who had faced the German flyers numerous times knew the dangers of any and all our enemies. Our own Canadian aces, men like Billy Bishop, Billy Barker, Raymond Collishaw or Donald MacLaren, understood the need to respect the enemy. As for my own friend Billy, he wasn't cocky — he wanted revenge.

Back at the aerodrome, we learned that it was indeed a new man, Collins, who had gone down. This was his first posting after training. He was nineteen years old.

Billy, Rogers and I stood just inside the hangar, three of us, with steaming tins of coffee.

"There are times I wish I had Bunyan's fists," Rogers said wistfully and glanced at Billy. "You're a bloody idiot, going after the Baron like that."

Billy only shrugged.

"He baited you," Rogers added. "Waited for one of us to pull away. Then went right at you."

Again Billy shrugged. "I've got my reasons. He's the one that went down, isn't he?"

"You're lucky," Rogers said seriously.

"What is luck?" Billy retorted. "You've either got the angels on your side like Stitch here, or it's off to hell like Collins today."

"Just stop trying to kill yourself," I said. "The Hun are good pilots. Their planes are ingenious and match or better our own. You know that. And for crying out loud, you just took down their best."

He nodded. "Didn't kill him though, did I? Captain says the Hun were fast to wire and say that the pilot landed without a scratch." He glanced at Rogers. "That must have been luck. It couldn't have been angels. He's on the other side."

"Beggin' yer pardons, sirs," came a voice from above, pulling us from our discussion. A mechanic leaned down from his ladder as he worked on a bent propeller. "I'm not a churchgoing man myself. But I do know there will be hell to pay if I don't fix this prop. Could one of you hand me that spanner?"

And that was the end of our discussion.

Chapter 12
April–May 1917

The next month became known as Bloody April. We flew even more than usual and I found myself getting a little careless when we entered dogfights. In the skies I felt less and less fear and far more exhilaration, as if the air itself were intoxicating. The very carelessness that we warned new pilots about was creeping into my day-to-day flying. On the ground I was bone-tired and often depressed. Sleep did not come easily, especially when some of our pilots did not return from sorties. I saw men die horribly that month. Both sides sustained a high rate of casualties. Every week we were raising our glasses to honour another fallen friend.

I became so sick of writing home, or to Nellie, about another death that I stopped recording them. Instead, I wrote about the soccer matches and the indescribable coffee that we adored in the French towns. More than anything I wrote about how dearly I wanted to see each of them.

On April 6 some shocking news arrived: the United States had finally declared war on Germany!

Angry at the Germans' continued use of U-boats against passenger and merchant ships, the United States was entering the fray. Needless to say, the news made a splash among the men.

"The Americans are boasting that they'll put twenty thousand planes in the air against the Hun," I heard one pilot say on our way out to the field.

"I'll believe it when I see it," said another.

Our captain snorted. "Won't help us today, will it? We could use a hundred more planes — and better ones — to face off against these wretched Albatroses."

I wrote to Sarah that night:

I wonder if this might mean the end of the war. America is a big country and the Germans must be shaking in their boots at this announcement. I only wish they had come sooner. There are a lot of good men who might still be alive. But if the United States entering the war allows me to go home, then I can only hope that they advance quickly. And if you are very good I might bring someone home with me.

Less than a week after America joined the Allies, we cheered when news came of the incredible Canadian victory at Vimy Ridge. They had taken a hill, a strategic and well-fortified high ground used by the enemy to rain down shells on Allied troops. Yet our elation began to die away when news of the number of casualties started to come out. The rumours said well over three thousand dead and up to ten thousand injured during the battle. It was still a stunning achievement, but at such cost.

* * *

Billy and I were so exhausted that by the third week of April, we were granted leave. Our service since January was deemed enough to warrant the rest, and our mistakes certainly showed that we both needed a break. In the last week alone, Billy had ruined the undercarriage of two planes while landing. Twice I had drifted into enemy territory, once with two inexperienced pilots under my protection.

At the time of the second incident I told myself that the wind was extreme and that I was just trying to hem in the new pilots. It was the partial truth. In fact, for several minutes I had stopped looking at my maps and at the landmarks for direction. It was a moment of fatigue, of "mind drifting" — a curse that plagued all of us when we were too tired. We were fortunate enough to return whole, with the new pilots intact, but it did not come as a great surprise when the commander decided that Billy and I needed a rest, or we were going to make more costly mistakes.

My intention was to get to Redcar and Grimsby as quickly as possible. The commander permitted us to fly a two-seater to England provided that we brought him something better than an old R.E.8 reconnaissance plane in return. It was much faster than taking the train and then the boat across the Channel and we jumped at the chance. Billy agreed to stay with me at Mrs. Baxter's. "It's about time I see that Nellie of yours again," he said.

On the field I looked over our transport with a critical eye. "Some caution with that beastie, if you please, sir," a mechanic said as he walked over to me. He wiped his greasy hands on an equally greasy cloth. "She's been sputtering a fair bit and is given to bouts of power loss. It's good that you're flying on our side, sir, or you'd be a sitting duck."

The R.E.8, nicknamed "Harry Tate," was often used for reconnaissance and photography missions. I had seen them many times on the base. They were steady machines, but had little manoeuvrability compared to our fighters. This particular Harry Tate had seen a great deal of action. Only a few days earlier, six R.E.8s had been tragically shot down near Douai by Jasta 11. The Baron had registered over 40 kills.

"Caution taken!" I answered and thanked him.

How could I explain that I would have flown it with one wing if it could take me to Nellie? And after months of constant stress and action, I cared little about the dangers of a slightly faulty plane travelling over friendly ground.

Billy stopped me as I tossed in my bag. "We're stopping in Middlesbrough."

"Why?"

"To pick up a ring, you twit."

And we did. I bought a gold band — slender, yet great in significance.

A few days into our leave Billy and I took the train to Grimsby.

"You look as if you're off to fight Jasta 11," Billy teased.

"It's a different sort of worry," I answered.

"Let me warm up the old man," he said. "I'll give you your cue."

We approached the farm at teatime and our arrival was greatly heralded. Billy fell right into telling stories, and within minutes he and Mr. Timpson were laughing and taking sips of beer. They wandered to the porch, where their voices quieted.

"That's curious," said Nellie as she eyed the two men through the window.

Standing in front of my beautiful Nellie, I nearly offered her the ring on the spot. I was saved by her youngest brother, who charged at me with his head down and tackled me.

"Off!" Nellie commanded him. I gave him a playful punch and let him go. As I stooped down to retrieve my hat it struck me like a thunderbolt that my head was exposed. Nellie reached out and touched my hair.

"Is that a wound?" she asked worriedly.

I was tempted to tell her a wild tale, but with Nellie that would never do. "It's a stress spot," I said. "The doctor says it's caused by tension and will grow back naturally enough. It's part of the reason I'm on leave."

She tapped her lips with her fingers and regarded me thoughtfully. Then she said, "If it doesn't grow back then I'd like you to shave a spot on the opposite side so that you match."

I laughed, pulled her to me and kissed her.

"Not here!" She giggled and looked around nervously.

The door to the porch opened and Billy beckoned. "Over here, Master Townend," he quipped.

I swallowed hard, glanced one more time at Nellie and then went out to the porch. Billy put a mug of beer in my hand. I took a swig without even thinking.

Mr. Timpson regarded me as he had the first

day I'd met him in his field, when he'd walked towards us carrying a shotgun. I took a second swig of beer. "Mr. Miller informs me you have something of importance to say."

I stared hard at the beer swirling in my mug. "Well, yes, sir. I do. I do have something of importance to ask you."

Billy stared at the porch.

"You may," Mr. Timpson said.

I choked on my beer. "I . . . I . . . may?"

"You may ask me this thing of importance."

Billy made an indistinguishable sound and wrapped his arms around his chest.

When I looked up at Mr. Timpson, I saw the tiniest creases in the corners of his eyes, the faintest hint of humour.

"Sir?" I asked stupidly.

He leaned forward and whispered. "Ask me."

"Would you permit me to marry your daughter?" I said.

Billy and Mr. Timpson burst out laughing and turned away from me to grasp each other's shoulders. When Mr. Timpson looked at me again, he had regained his composure. "With my blessings, my boy," he said. "There's not much to think about on the farm in January and February, and Mrs. Timpson's been chatting up the topic non-stop."

I set down my beer to shake his hand, and then reached down to pick it back up, in the same instant that he offered his own hand. Eventually we managed to shake hands. Nellie appeared at the door, watching us curiously.

"Go," Mr. Timpson said to me and nodded towards his daughter. I took Nellie outside in the gathering dusk, knelt in the mud and asked her to marry me. Mr. Timpson agreed to our marriage when Nellie turned nineteen, in less than a year's time.

It was difficult to leave the farm that evening. The whole family accompanied us to the station for the last train. When I kissed Nellie goodbye, she did not pull away or appear embarrassed as she had earlier that night. Our lives had changed with the coming of a slender ring that sat so beautifully on her finger.

* * *

Our return to France was considerably different than our departure. In the first place, I felt a wave of hope through my engagement to Nellie. It somehow eased the weight of the war. For almost an entire day my hand stopped shaking. I wrote to my parents and to Robert with the news and could hardly wait for their replies. The shaking returned, however, when we received word that we were to ferry a fighter over to an RNAS base at Dunkirk.

The Bristol F.2b fighter was a powerful beast and superior to the Harry Tate. It had a Vickers forward-firing machine gun for the pilot and a twin Lewis machine gun on a Scarff ring for the rear cockpit. The Scarff ring ran around the perimeter of the cockpit like an elevated miniature train track, allowing the gunner a great deal of manoeuvrability in order to shoot at the enemy.

Billy was wide awake this time and somewhat refreshed, although he was still exhausted. He certainly looked better after long hours of sleep and Mrs. Baxter's cooking. And my engagement to Nellie had become a feather in his cap.

"Couldn't have done it without me, Paulie," he boasted. "I had the old man eating out of my palm. You're lucky I didn't decide to marry the girl myself."

I experimented with the Bristol F.2b while travelling over the Channel, rolling and banking more often than Billy liked. "It's a good plane," I shouted.

"Yes, it is," he roared back. "And as revenge for your stomach-turning tricks, I ate the rest of Mrs. Baxter's cookies. Hurrah!"

Our new orders were to ferry yet another plane, this time a Bristol wanted at Dieppe, and then find transport back to our squadron. It was a smooth flight and without incident.

On delivering the Bristol, we were informed of our reassignment to a squadron near Dunkirk.

"I wonder what they're flying over at Dunkirk," Billy commented.

"Pups, most likely," I answered.

"I meant the Hun."

* * *

In May, news of British ace Albert Ball's death reached us at Dunkirk and kept us all sombre for days. The word around the aerodrome was that he'd flown into a cloud and then crashed to the ground. Exactly why he'd crashed was still unknown. He'd been a brilliant pilot, the pride of the Royal Flying Corps, scoring 44 victories. The British officers were crushed by the news.

Late that month came the rumour of daylight bombing raids against England. The threat called for increased caution along the coasts.

Daylight bombing was risky, as the anti-aircraft gunners could easily see the planes. But the Hun had created an agile new bomber, the Gotha, and they had confidence in their aircraft. On May 25, the Gothas attacked the English coast and the town of Folkstone, killing over ninety civilians.

Chapter 13
June–September 1917

In early June we received exciting news. We were to be outfitted with new planes, Sopwith Camels, a newer version of the Pup. U-boats were making more frequent appearances in the English Channel and we needed planes that could take on both the German air and undersea power. Rumour spread quickly that the Camel was a better fighter than the Albatros. There was also a rumour that the Camel came with surprises. Those surprises turned out to be both a blessing and a curse.

The skies were clear and the temperature warm on the day the new planes arrived. They were a marvellous sight — five biplanes with a mysterious hump, a camel's hump, in front of the pilot. The hump turned out to be two Vickers machine guns, covered by a piece of metal designed to make the plane more streamlined and reduce drag.

"Looks a little odd," Billy commented as we inspected the planes.

"No, no," I said. "Look at it! They've put the engine, guns, pilot and fuel in a compact little box.

No more than six or seven feet, I'd say. That will make it feel like riding a horse even more than the Pup."

Billy shook his head doubtfully.

I stood at the prop and paced off towards the tail, squatting under the wing and then coming to a stop just past the cockpit. "There," I said. "No more than seven feet. That's going to make for excellent manoeuvrability if the engine's got any pluck."

"That's a point, isn't it?" he answered. "It really is compact."

By the end of the day the pilots were called in for a briefing. Two British officers delivered a summary of the plane's operation, and their expressions set an ominous tone.

"The Camel carries its centre of gravity far forward," one officer began. "The engine, pilot, weaponry — are all at the front. A full fuel tank can be particularly hazardous in disrupting the centre of gravity," he went on. "Be wary of it, especially on quick takeoffs when ground crew has fuelled you. Do not let the excitement of the Camel's power lull you. You must keep her steady with concerted pressure on the rudder and ailerons." He looked at each of us intently. "We've lost pilots already in training. Too many."

The officer clasped his hands behind his back.

"Which raises yet another point. The Camel's rotary engine carries a gyroscopic effect — a strong one! She'll pull hard to the right, so be ready to compensate or you'll find yourself upside down before you've left the ground."

Billy stirred beside me. "Is the news all bad then, sir?" he asked.

The officer shook his head. "Not at all. The same torque that hurls you over on takeoff is the very power that will make your manoeuvrability in the air go well beyond anything the Hun has to offer. The test pilots have fallen in love with this plane. Those that have survived," he added.

Despite the warnings I found myself restless to get into the cockpit. The Camel looked and sounded exciting. I understood the dangers and I knew I would keep them in mind when operating the plane. Instead of anxiety I felt the same wild surge of excitement that I'd felt when flying with my instructors back at Curtiss.

"I want to get up there," I said to Billy when we returned to our huts.

"You'll get your chance," he answered, with less enthusiasm. "We all will."

* * *

It was mid-June before I had my first flight in a Camel. The cockpit had a wicker seat, and rudder controls up near the engine. I marvelled at the twin Vickers and watched two crewmen load the guns. One man sat in the cockpit while another stood on the ground and unfolded the belt of bullets.

"Might want to be careful with this one, sir," the crewman in the cockpit said. "Almost turned over yesterday."

"Was it on a full fuel tank?" I asked.

The man stopped loading bullets to think. "I believe it was, sir. We fuelled it first thing, at about seven, and the pilot went up around nine for a spin. There'll be plenty of fuel left, if that's what you mean. Shall I check for you?"

There was just over half a tank in the Camel when the crew prepared me for takeoff. The engine roared and I laughed at the power surging through the plane, from my seat to my feet at the rudder controls. I signalled thumbs-up and two crewmen took hold of either wing. I increased throttle and began to move. The men trotted beside me, steadying the wings. They ran me out about 50 feet or so and then let go. The torque of the engine, pulling hard to the right, was unbelievably strong. I pushed my rudder out full to compensate and then opened the throttle wide.

There was a steady spurt of castor oil spray, more so than with the Pup, or at least more of it actually hitting me, and I wiped my goggles clear with my scarf.

As I gained speed, bumping and teetering along the field, I had to keep my foot pressed hard on the rudder. The torque was powerful, and without the countering rudder, the plane would have careened to the right and crashed into the trucks parked alongside the landing field.

As my wheels left the ground the wings suddenly dipped in a gust of wind and I eased off the rudder to compensate. The torque pulled me right back up and would have flipped me over onto the field like a pancake if I hadn't pressed my foot back down on that rudder. I grinned. She was a feisty beast!

At 500 feet I started to test the Camel. I completed a slow turn to the left and gained more altitude. There was certainly nothing remarkable about the Camel banking to port. Then I turned to starboard and felt the instant change. She wanted to turn — and with a will! The controls were light and responsive, and with the compact nature of the cockpit and engine, I felt in complete command.

"It *is* like riding a horse!" I shouted. At 800 feet I rolled her over twice in succession. I performed a loop and even fired the twin Vickers to gain a feel for the weaponry. The plane was a marvel.

That night in my cot I drew an elaborate sketch

of the Camel. I loved the compact feeling of the airplane, for it delivered such a wonderful sense of control. Soon it would be time to try the Camel in combat. I finished the sketch with a flyer's scarf trailing far behind. In the centre of the scarf I wrote: *All for Nellie!*

* * *

The fellows celebrated my twentieth birthday in August with aviators' flair. They decked me out in winter gear, including gloves and goggles, and then proceeded to put a cake that someone had brought in from town on my lap. I discovered later that it was Billy's mad scheme, and I provided a good deal of amusement with my attempts to get the cake into my mouth.

My parents sent me a tin of candies and coffee — all of which were gone by the end of the day. Nellie sent me a letter that set my heart racing. She also sent a pound of chocolate. I couldn't imagine how she'd managed to do that, but guessed that perhaps her father had chipped in to help.

"Where are you two pigeons going to live?" Billy asked me one day. "England? Will you work for her father? Or will you take her back to Canada? There's no war there, you know."

"I don't know," I said truthfully. "I haven't thought about that."

"Well, you'd better," he answered.

His words got me thinking and I asked Nellie about it in my next letter. We were so caught up in the idea of marriage that other details seemed insignificant at the time. The war dragged on and I wondered if there would ever come a time when we might be married in peace. I knew what my sister Sarah would say. She wanted us safely at the farm near Winnipeg — perhaps in a little house on the upper pasture. But what did Nellie want?

* * *

One evening in September we were given orders to stand ready just past nine o'clock. A wire from the coast alerted us that planes had been spotted heading towards London. A second wire came through minutes later. *Gotha bombers.*

Billy was not called up. He twirled his moustache at me. "Don't get yourself shot!"

Six Camels were running and ready for us as we jogged out to the field. The other five pilots were British, lads I knew only from our soccer games. The senior officer, Newkirk, was a year or two older than me. We'd had a brief discussion on the sideline during one match. He was not impressed with the torque of the Camel and confessed that it troubled him greatly — it might be especially tricky for the newer pilots.

As we ran the last few yards to the planes in the dark, the adrenaline pumped through my body. A night flight in a Camel! And against a foe as well! This wasn't just a training sequence. Curiously, my hand did not shake.

The castor oil spurted as I settled into my seat and attached the safety belt. I checked my scarf to make sure it was wrapped properly and ready for use. It was going to be a hunt in the dark to find the Gothas and we needed our ears and eyes wide open.

I brought my plane in behind Newkirk and let him move forward before opening the throttle. Each plane was to take off several minutes in advance of the next, for safety. There was a good deal of dust, but I could still see his wings in the moonlight.

Only 10 feet from the ground, Newkirk's wing suddenly dipped to port, just as mine had done on my first flight in a Camel. As he compensated, his wing came over hard to starboard and he couldn't bring it back up in time. The wing caught the ground and raised a storm of dust. In a split second the plane performed a grotesque cartwheel, spinning end over end until it collapsed in a mess of wood and canvas.

"Poor old Newkirk," I gasped. There was no hope of him being alive, not with that sort of crash. The glow and flicker of flames rose up from the field. Seconds later there was an explosion. Flames shot up high into the night. I slammed my hand on the console.

For a moment I wondered what to do. We had lost not only a pilot, but also our leader. Behind me, the other planes were lining up. Without Newkirk, I was next in command. As I stared at the fire burning on the field, I thought of the Gothas on their way across the Channel and of the deaths that would result from their bombing. I slammed the console one more time. Then I increased throttle and took off, making for the Channel. The mission had to carry on.

It was cloudy but with relatively decent visibility. The clouds were stacked more ominously along the coast towards northern France and Germany. The Hun was brazen to fly on such a night, clearly unafraid of reprisals and confident of their own strength in the air. Word had it before we left that there were other sorties going up from squadrons in the area, so we were not alone. I grimaced. It could be trouble with too many planes. Even with the moon slipping out from the clouds, it was often impossible to see an enemy clearly until he was close, or the silhouette of the plane was outlined in relief.

We were not even halfway across the Channel when I spotted dots in the sky headed northeast towards Europe. I made to intercept, knowing the others would be doing the same. I did not doubt that Newkirk's crash was emblazoned on their minds and that their hands were itchy for revenge. The best remedy for a loss was a win.

The dots ahead grew closer. They must have seen us, for they changed course — not markedly, but enough to go around us should we lose them in the infrequent clouds.

As they moved I caught sight of the giant engines on either side of the fuselage. They were Gothas all right — seven of them. There didn't appear to be any accompanying fighters, which was not surprising, given the distance they had covered and the size of their fuel tanks compared to a single-seater. The Gothas were agile for their size and carried a versatile rear gun on the back. When they travelled in significant numbers, as they were doing now, it made their guns that much more lethal. They could lay down a wide and accurate suppressing fire from all seven planes before we could break up the pack.

I realized that some were changing course, not to escape as much as to provide their rear gunners with a good view of us. I increased altitude. We had the edge on the Gothas in terms of speed. Our Camels could do over 115 miles per hour, whereas the Gothas' top speed was little more than 85. There were larger cloud formations ahead that would play into the bombers' advantage and we needed to attack before it became a game of hide-and-seek.

As we cleared the first cloud mass, the rear gunners fired. White lines of smoke traced through the night sky towards us. To keep from presenting a good target, I kept my plane moving from side to side as I neared the bombers. At about 200 yards I gave the central plane three solid bursts.

I discovered a problem. The flashes from the incendiary bullets coming from my own machine gun were absolutely blinding. Even when I turned my head, I saw a thousand stars swirling in the darkness. To make matters worse, it dawned on me that the flashes from my gun made me an excellent target. There was nothing to be done about it other than to make myself as difficult a target as possible and to squint when I fired.

I dropped a little and fired a burst, then rose up again just as quickly and fired another. What an annoying fly I must have been to that gunner — biting at his flesh with each burst and yet so hard to swat! My attack must have caused some damage, for the central plane broke away from the others and headed down towards a cloud bank at some 8000 feet. The Gotha pilot was trying to lose me in the clouds — the very game I feared we would end up playing. I followed, firing almost incessantly and stopping only to keep my gun from jamming.

It was the longest burst I had given, and my eyes were so blinded from the machine-gun flashes that I lost sight of the Gotha completely. I gained altitude and stared out into the darkness, waiting for my night vision to return. It took a good 30 seconds before I was seeing well enough. Still, I couldn't spot the bomber anywhere. I listened intently for sounds outside of my own plane. The Gotha might have dropped even lower in a bid to escape. Against the blackness of the sea it would be invisible unless the moon came out again. I broke off the chase and headed back to join the others.

The remainder of the Gotha pack had maintained their formation despite the constant strafing from the other Camels. I could see the lines of fiery bullets coming from two of our planes, narrowly missing the top wing of the port-side Gotha. The other bombers turned their guns and concentrated their fire.

"Get under him, get under him!" I shouted. In a cloudless portion of the sky where I could see the bomber clearly, one of the Camels did a tricky little flip and banked to port, out of the line of fire.

"Cheeky!" I shouted. The other Camel went under the Gotha as if he had miraculously heard me yelling. It was a close call for both of them. And where in the world were those other Camels? They were nowhere to be seen.

Our battle drifted towards the same giant cumulous cloud into which the first Gotha had disappeared moments before, and the others decided to follow suit. I was nearly on them again, at full throttle.

The two missing Camels came into sight a moment later. In a brilliant move they had sped ahead of the bombers, to loop back and come straight on, firing burst after burst. The sky was alight with incendiary bullet trails. In the meantime I caught up and strafed the rear gunners while my mates took them from the front.

Bullets whistled round my head. Incendiary trails stemmed from two different Gothas, making it clear that I had become the focus of their attention. In another second they would find their mark.

I rolled my Camel over to starboard. She flipped as easily as a seal in the water. When I came round, I realized that I was closer to the bombers than I had intended. I opened fire and managed two full bursts before sliding underneath them.

The Gothas had almost reached the cloud when another thought struck me — fuel. With all our tricks and manoeuvres we had expended a great deal of it. We could only fly for two and a half hours on a full tank, while the Gothas were good for five.

I came round again and joined two other Camels. We dove on the last Gotha, entering the cloud like crows after an eagle. The rear gunner fired madly at all three of us. We kept ourselves spaced from one another, with enough room to flit back and forth to avoid fire. One of us — it looked like the pilot on my starboard side — got in a good burst that ran up from the Gotha's tail to the cockpit. The gunner stopped shooting.

"Got you!" I yelled triumphantly and fired another burst. One of the Gotha's giant engines began to smoke, and just as the bomber entered the cloud I saw it lose power on the starboard side. It fell slowly, coasting along the edge of the wispy white cloud and in and out of our vision.

Suddenly it appeared again, its nose down, one engine burning like a fireball. When the Gotha disappeared into the darkness of a cloud bank below, I turned for home. Whether or not the bomber crashed, I could not tell, but it was most certainly earthbound.

It had been a short, sharp battle and we returned with five of our six fighters intact. The Camels performed well, and if it had not been for Newkirk's loss, it would have been a perfect night. It was the first time I had commanded an attack and I was thankful to have all four planes land safely behind me.

"Bloody good fight!" said one of the pilots as he thumped me on the back.

"I couldn't see a damned thing whenever I fired my gun," another added. "My eyes were full of stars."

"We've got to do something about that," I answered. "It will get us killed some night unless we do. Brilliant move to come back and attack from the front!" We shook hands and clapped one another's backs.

As we crossed the field our celebrations ceased. The twisted remains of Newkirk's plane lay heaped by the side of the hangar.

Chapter 14
September–November 1917

We saw regular action right through to the end of September. To our delight, Rogers was transferred to our squadron. There was much to say. We spent several evenings staying up late and talking. I'd never drunk so much coffee in my life.

"Tying the knot, young man!" Rogers teased me. "Well, it's about time. You talk about her enough."

I also heard from Robert. He wrote from a hospital where he was recovering from another round of trench foot. He was a sergeant now. He wrote sparingly and I could tell he simply did not want to waste words on the horrors he'd confronted. He focused on our farm and, like Billy, asked about where Nellie and I would live. To my own surprise I wrote back: *If Nellie wants it, I'd be pleased for us to have a farm somewhere near Winnipeg, close enough to all of you.*

I could only hope that all of us would one day meet together safely. I desperately wanted my parents and Sarah to meet Nellie face to face. And of course, I wanted everyone to meet Billy.

Billy had come to love the Sopwith Camel. His initial hesitations were eliminated after his first flight. He and the Camel were made for each other, although I often felt he was a little too confident with the manoeuvres he attempted. He could flip his Camel so easily to pull out of nasty situations that he began to rely on the trick rather heavily. In short order he scored 4 victories, mostly Albatros D.V.s and one Albatros two-seater, bringing his total to 7.

On a crisp, clear October morning, four of us went up on patrol. No more than 3 minutes from takeoff, Rogers caught my attention. Instinctively I glanced above. The sky was clear. Rogers shook his head. He put his arm outside of the cockpit and pointed down. We were only 2000 feet above the Channel and the water was covered in a light chop. It was tricky to see anything clearly with the whitecaps setting the ocean in motion. I stared closely and caught sight of what Rogers was pointing at. Something was coming out of the water half a mile from the shore, an oblong black shape.

"A U-boat," I muttered to myself. "Rogers, you found us a submarine!" I waved to indicate that I'd spotted it.

He gave me a thumbs-up and banked sharply.

The rest of us followed. As we descended I

wondered what we were going to do. The ground crew had not loaded bombs into my plane that morning, as there had been a problem with the detaching mechanism. One of the others might have bombs, but I'd be reduced to strafing. There were several ships in the area and we needed to alert them immediately. The top of the U-boat tower was well out of the water and they would soon be aware of us.

Rogers dove steeply and we buzzed right over the conning tower. We circled above it, drawing attention from our nearby ships. Sailors on them began running. Alarm bells sounded. There was no need to spell out what was happening; the sailors knew, the instant we began circling. A small destroyer was already in the area, steaming our way, though less than a mile from Dunkirk. I could see the smoke from its stack as it rushed to the scene. The U-boat must have noticed us too. It began to submerge.

We attacked on the next flyby, each of us strafing the disappearing conning tower. Little if anything happened. Our bullets struck the water without effect. I felt so helpless without any bombs and I determined from that moment never to fly without them again. We could still see the giant shape of the U-boat below the surface, but it was quickly going deeper.

By the time the destroyer reached us, the U-boat had completely disappeared.

There was a great deal of bustle aboard the destroyer. A collection of what looked like large oil drums was gathered at its stern. Our ship slowed down and one after another of the drums was released into the sea, precisely where we had last seen the U-boat. I knew the drums were depth charges loaded with highly explosive TNT, and that they were effective up to 300 feet below the surface. I wondered how deep the U-boat had managed to go before the destroyer arrived.

We continued to circle, searching a wider area, but the submarine was nowhere to be seen.

Moments later there was a series of explosions as the depth charges blew. Enormous water spouts erupted. It was quite a sight from the air. Sailors onboard the destroyer watched, leaning over the rails to spot any sign of success. We too watched and waited. Several men pointed and there appeared to be some excitement. Then the gesturing stopped and the sailors went back to their positions.

Rogers took us for a lengthy pass up and down Dunkirk's coast before heading home. We found out on our return that the destroyer had successfully blown up a passing school of fish. The U-boat escaped, likely unscathed, although there was no way of knowing for certain. But the experience made me aware of how important our job was. We were the eyes of defence — in the air and on the sea.

* * *

On the night of November 2 we were told to stand ready, as enemy planes had been spotted heading down the Belgian coast for England, possibly Gotha bombers. Eight of us prepared for a sortie. There was a great deal of cloud covering the moon that night, which gave the Germans an advantage against anti-aircraft fire. They'd chosen the night for their raid well.

Rogers went up first — he was now commander of our unit and our most respected pilot.

"Not too close," he had shouted above the roar as the first Camel started up. "There's a lot of us and vision will be tricky. Give me four or five minutes before you follow." He gave me a gentle punch in the arm.

"Good luck, Stitch!" called Billy. I waved over to him.

Takeoff was the easiest thing that happened that night. There was little time to lose, as the enemy had the advantage of altitude and it would take some time for us to match them. As planned,

I kept the throttle open, gaining altitude and hoping to intercept the bombers based on the last information we'd had on the ground. In truth, it was like chasing shadows, but there was little choice and we made the best of it.

Halfway across the Channel I saw Rogers ahead of me when the clouds broke, and I kept him in sight. The others behind me were doing the same, for when I looked back I caught a glimpse of at least two planes. Rogers headed up to 10,000 feet and banked to starboard, cutting back in towards the Belgian coast. He was creating a zigzag pattern in the hope that we might spot the enemy, just as if we were hunting for a lost plane, or a lost person in the forest. It was in the next turn towards the English side that I spotted our quarry. They were above me, dotted like black stars spread out against the sky. I counted nine for certain, although there could have been more.

I increased altitude and aimed for an intercept. If they were Gothas, then I wanted to avoid a rear attack, if possible, having learned from our previous engagement. Clouds got in the way as we rose higher, and I lost sight of the enemy numerous times. Once I entered the thickest clouds I kept turning to search for friend and foe alike, hoping that others were doing the same. Billy suddenly appeared on my port side as we shot out into a clear space.

Rogers was either brilliant or extremely lucky, for our timing could not have been better. He and I emerged from the cloud with the Hun straight ahead.

They spotted us and gained further altitude, rising above the remaining clouds and into clear sky. We matched their altitude and kept straight on towards them. I flexed my hands and got ready to fight. The Gotha silhouette against the cloud looked like an enormous dragonfly. As the enemy grew nearer, I opened fire and watched the trail of my bullets rip through the night towards them. Their return fire came just as fiercely from the fore gunner, so I immediately flitted from side to side to avoid taking a hit.

I continued straight ahead and flew over top of the bomber, then looked behind me. Billy, on my left flank and a little below, performed his favourite roll to starboard. As he flipped beneath me I saw that another Gotha had also lowered altitude, but to port, opposite of his fellows. It was a split-second decision, an instinct made by both pilots at the same time as they drove towards the same spot in the sky. There was a clacking sound beneath me, the likes of which I had never heard before, followed by a burst of flame. I craned over the starboard side of the cockpit, fearing the worst.

In the flaring light I saw two planes, barely visible and rapidly disappearing. One spiralled down towards the Channel while the other wobbled precariously, heading back towards the coast. In the darkness I couldn't tell which was which.

The plane spiralling towards the earth must have taken the worst of the crash, for it went straight down and I could see no sign of it pulling out of the dive. The other pilot was at least headed in the right direction. It gave me hope, since Billy, and not the Hun, would likely make for France. Just as I was about to turn and chase after the fleeing plane in the hope of finding Billy, I came upon one of the bombers.

The air whistled with bullets and my Camel was soon pressed to its limits, flipping, banking and strafing. In the light of our bullet trails and one flaming engine of a bomber, a Gotha pilot stared straight at me as I buzzed over him. I came right in between two others of our group, all of us firing but managing to miss each other. We were so close that the gunners were forced to stop firing as I passed.

Then something white-hot struck the side of my head. The pain was so excruciating I wondered if a bullet had gone through my skull. The blow knocked me over to the starboard side of the cockpit, where I sat stunned for several seconds. I stared dizzily at the instrument panel, but the battle was still hot around me and I sat up. Instinctively I fired burst after burst until I was clear of the bombers.

Decreasing throttle, I looked to see if there was any pursuit, but the darkness remained complete behind me. I sucked in several deep breaths and rested my forehead on one hand. Searing pain followed by deep throbbing wracked the side of my skull. I touched the wound and then brought my hand down to the dim lights of my instrument panel. My fingers came back slippery with blood.

I removed my helmet, undid my scarf, wrapped it tightly around my chin and tied it off. Then I replaced the helmet and hoped I'd stanched the worst of the bleeding. Tightening my chinstrap helped stabilize my head. When I stared at my instrument panel to check the state of my plane, though, the gauges blurred. I was suddenly quite dizzy and needed to vomit.

With my head pounding, I turned the plane around. It was at that instant that I blacked out. One moment I was headed back to the battle; the next I was in a nosedive, headed for the English

Channel. I had fallen forward with my head resting on the instrument panel. The wind was ferocious, shaking me as I tried to sit up. I felt exhausted and wanted only to put my head back down.

"Up!" I commanded myself, fighting through the grogginess. The blackout must not have lasted long, for my engine was still running and I was not going very fast. I reached forward and eased back on the stick. I adjusted the flaps, still fighting the wind and gravitational pull. Slowly, very slowly, the plane came back under my control. I was down to 4000 feet and it suddenly came clear to me how close I'd been to crashing.

I levelled off, made a slow bank around, and began to climb again. Questions plagued me. Had I lost too much blood? Had my brain been injured? My disorientation seemed to grow by the minute. I breathed deeply several more times to settle my racing heart. It was in that moment that I decided to head back to France. I couldn't risk another blackout — especially in the heat of battle — and endanger my companions. My duty was to return the plane and myself to base in sound condition, rather than be a hindrance to the sortie.

By the time I reached the coastline, I remembered Billy. I started to turn around. Then I remembered the plane headed for France. If Billy's plane was damaged and he had turned back to base, then my returning to battle was wasted. But if Billy's plane was the one that went down . . . No! I did not let myself think about it.

I felt steadily weaker as I progressed along the coast. In addition to the pain in my head and my nauseated stomach, there was a deeper fear growing inside me. Landing a plane in the dark was as dangerous as fighting an enemy at night. How was I going to land without all my faculties in proper working order?

I sat up straighter. *Pull it together, Stitch. Let's do this right. Be alert! Be awake!* I sang a song and pushed the pain away as far as I could. I retightened the scarf and my chinstrap in the hope of slowing the blood loss. The land was a black mass below. I stared until my eyes ached.

Soon another problem began to worry at me. Where was the base? Had I passed it already? All I could make out below was the dim phosphorescence off the sea, distinguishing water from land. Over the past few months we had patrolled the coast over and over again, so I hunted for every promontory and headland that looked familiar.

I dropped altitude, coming down extremely low along the water in the hope of finding some sort of feature that would help me locate the base.

My head continued to throb and I had to retighten the scarf several more times.

Increasing altitude again, I turned and went back up the coast. Still there was nothing, although one of the headlands looked vaguely familiar. The base had to be somewhere nearby.

In my dizzy condition, I couldn't remember when we'd set out, or even how long I had been up. There was still fuel in the tank and I took courage from that.

Some time later I made the decision to go inland and attempt to find a field if the base didn't present itself in the next few minutes. It was not the best option, for there was little certainty of landing, and even less certainty of landing on friendly soil. But only a minute elapsed before I spotted, less than a mile ahead, a series of little lights outlining a safe landing area on the field.

I recognized the tiny lamps that the ground crew set out when visibility was particularly poor, placing gas-covered rags in small cans to help pilots find their way. The lights wouldn't stay lit long, for fear of a U-boat in the harbour or bombers coming our way. I came down rather clumsily and in a hurry.

"Too fast," I muttered and eased up the throttle. I'd try again. I headed farther out into the

Channel, made a slow bank and came around. When the beach came up too quickly I was forced to turn again for another try.

"Focus, focus," I told myself. It was difficult to estimate the distance, especially when my head was so foggy. On my next try I cleared the beach and approached the lighted field.

"Rudder, rudder!" I shouted at myself. Even the sound of my own voice made me wince. This time, patches of grass and dirt were visible between the flickering lights. I brought the Camel down as slowly as I could and wrestled the controls to keep her steady. The tiny lights came up suddenly and I realized too late that I was still approaching too quickly.

I gritted my teeth. "Now or never!" With a crunch and a terrific jolt, my undercarriage broke away. I did not pull up, however, and bumped and slid along the field within the perimeter of the lights. The jolting was horrific and I felt another blackout coming. When the Camel finally came to a full stop I switched the engine off and put my aching head in my hands. I was on the ground. Hallelujah, I was down.

"Are you all right, sir?" someone shouted. Helping hands lifted me out of the cockpit. A bright light shone in my face.

"Blimey," someone murmured. Then, "Medic! Medic!"

I was loaded onto a truck and someone rode with me, pressing a cloth firmly against my head.

"My head," I murmured. "It hurts."

"You'll be right as rain, sir!" the man said. "But let's just keep your helmet on, shall we, until we reach the hospital? Looks as if a bullet's grazed your head, based on the hole in your helmet." One of the ground crew came up and handed me my flight jacket.

"Was there anyone that landed ahead of me?" I asked him.

He shook his head. "No, sir. You're the first one back."

Chapter 15
November 1917–March 1918

For three days we waited for news of Billy. At night I was restless, stirring at every sound, and hoping beyond hope that, like Ashcroft, Billy might show up and surprise us all. He did not come. My head throbbed. Rogers visited me regularly at the base hospital. He made me go over the incident minute by minute, and along with the rest of the men that night, we pieced together as accurate an account as we could.

To the best of our knowledge, Billy and the Albatros had suffered a mid-air collision, a fatal one as far as Billy was concerned. The Albatros apparently recovered sufficiently to fly, although it didn't return to the fray. Billy's plane spiralled down to the English Channel. No one else saw the incident, although Rogers witnessed the Albatros flying away from us. I had been the last to see Billy. I described the sound I had heard to the officers and to several of our mechanics and sail makers. Each of them said the sound appeared consistent with what a mid-air collision between two wood and fabric structures would make. One of the mechanics suggested that the undercarriage of the Albatros may have clipped Billy's wings. The Albatros could still fly without its undercarriage, but Billy would be helpless if a portion of both wings was ruined.

"Mid-airs aren't frequent," the mechanic said. "Yet often fatal when they do happen. I'm sorry, sir."

Talking about my best friend only made his absence that much greater. For months he had been telling me that he felt his end was near. I began to wonder if he had even set up my engagement with Nellie out of fear that he wouldn't be around to help me in the future. I always brushed off his fears. Death was all around us, and yet somehow, I'd felt that Billy would always make it.

I had never cried in the pilot's seat. Never shed a tear in the most harrowing moments or in the pain of being shot. But I cried for Billy and felt no shame in it.

In the end, I wrote a letter to his family. I do not remember the contents of the letter, for those few days were blurry and miserable, except that I included details of the crash. I also wrote something about my friendship with Billy and what an honour it was to have known him. Rogers wrote a letter as well, both as the commander of our squadron and a friend. He kept up his visits to the base hospital through those difficult days, saying little but making sure I ate.

* * *

My own condition was dismal. The nausea and vomiting continued for days. It was a bad concussion despite the fact that the wound on my skull itself was not deep. Being grounded was maddening, for I wanted every day to go back up into the skies and seek revenge for Billy. Eventually the doctors recommended a furlough in England, as I was not fit to fly until the symptoms went away.

This time I stayed with Nellie's family on the farm, and it was only under her care that I finally began to climb out of both the injury and the depression. I mended fences in the chilly wind, enjoying the change of using rocks rather than wood as we did in Canada. I cleaned out the cow stalls and smelled the familiar barn odours that had been a part of my daily life until joining the RNAS. The work was refreshing and tough, a welcome relief from the stress of the last days.

Nellie and I went for long walks, planning and enjoying our future lives together. She was not afraid to talk about Billy. Rather, she encouraged me to tell stories about him. The more I spoke, the more I felt that his memory was being honoured.

Somehow, through our walking and late-night talks, the wound of Billy's loss began to close. It did not heal, but at least it did not gape so agonizingly as it had in the first days and weeks.

Our conversations wandered to topics that Billy had pressed me about days before his death. It seemed uncanny that he had predicted such an end. Nellie wrestled with the prospect of leaving England and yet felt so much excitement over the idea of living in Canada. Both our parents had offered to build a cottage that would serve until we could make our own way. My parents wrote such a comforting letter that I felt a great relief about our future plans.

My head was bandaged for those weeks, and once, when Nellie was changing the dressing, she said, "You have a stress spot on this side and a long streak on the other. If you weren't about to become my husband I'd suggest we shape them both into a tonsure and declare you a monk!"

* * *

I returned to duty in mid-December. Rogers was on leave and I found the place rather dull without him or Billy. I played soccer when the field was not a mud bath, under doctor's orders not use my head to strike the ball.

One small and yet significant detail came to light

the first day I went up for patrol after my furlough. The ground crew gathered around my plane in the morning and welcomed me back. I was surprised by the greeting and very pleased. They grinned and I wondered what else was up.

"Well, sir," said a mechanic, "we've taken the liberty of adding a wee detail to your plane."

I glanced over the Camel and suddenly caught his meaning. Painted below the lip of the cockpit in bright white letters was one word: *Hurrah!*

I shook hands with each of the men, barely able to keep my voice from cracking.

"He was a good man, sir," a crewman said.

"He was a good man," I repeated. I put my hands on my hips and stared at them. "Well, gentlemen," I said. "In light of your good example, what say we call this Camel *Hurrah!*" The name stuck, and while I didn't always have the opportunity to fly the same plane, it was common knowledge that *Hurrah!* was mine. Further, I made it my duty to inform new pilots of the namesake and the memory of an excellent man, my dearest friend, Billy.

* * *

The rain, fog and ice in January kept us grounded for much of the month. We often stood ready to go out on patrol for hours, only to have the sortie called off. It was infuriating.

To keep busy and flying, I volunteered to take up photographers for reconnaissance. The planes were not half as fun as a Pup or Camel, but at least I was in the air and not sitting around in our hut. We didn't venture out far, however, without fighters.

When Rogers returned from leave, we clapped one another on the shoulders and then stood staring in silence as the gravity of the moment sank in — we had not seen one another since my concussion. Billy's death was a heavy burden to bear and there were days I could hardly stand it. Rogers put it best: "Some chaps make such an impact in life that their loss is no less great in death." I could only nod in agreement.

Rogers was delighted to see *Hurrah!*, and the following morning he painted his own memorial. *Billy's Vengeance* was towed out beside my plane and the ground crew all crowded in for a photograph.

With the weather co-operating, we managed regular patrols throughout February whenever the cloud ceiling remained high. On February 22, 1918, five of us went up at dusk in response to a warning that bombers were headed over the Channel.

It was a remarkable night. There was a bit of cloud cover and unusually warm air. As we climbed higher, the remaining sunlight burst from a bank of cloud clinging to the horizon. The light opened a path across the sea and I sighed at the glorious sight. It filled me with a longing for the wretched war to be over. I wanted to fly right over the Channel to Grimsby and land in the Timpsons' field. I thought of Robert and hoped beyond hope that he might make it safely through the war. The thought of losing both Billy and my brother was unbearable. Robert had not written for some time and there was no word from Sarah about him. Never before had I hoped so strongly for an end to the war. It was a lonely world when so many died so quickly. The sunlight dissolved into night and we returned to base without finding our quarry.

The next few days were a washout because of bad weather. When the sun finally came back, Rogers spoke with me at our soccer game. "We need some photos taken," he said. "It means flying the Big Ack. Are you up for it?"

I nodded. The Big Ack, or the Armstrong Whitworth F.K.8, was a lumbering multi-purpose plane that I had seen numerous times in the bay. It looked ungainly with its snub nose and long wings, but it could still manage 95 miles per hour and reach over 12,000 feet — more than enough to manage some reconnaissance.

"I'm always up for trying new planes," I answered.

Rogers grinned. "That's why I asked you." His

grin diminished. "It means flying into Belgium. You'll have an escort of four fighters."

I shook his hand. "You know I'm good for it. When do we go?"

A couple of days later, five of us made for the Belgian border. The four Camels around me looked so magnificent compared to the Big Ack and I couldn't help but shrug helplessly at Rogers as we made our way to the south of Ostend. He held his arm out and imitated flexing a muscle. Then he pointed at Big Ack. Yes, we were bigger, and we carried enough bombs to cause considerable damage if needed. The photographer, a fellow by the name of Tyler and a man of few words, made a great show of strapping himself into his seat.

We made excellent progress without being contested along the coast. The conditions were perfect for reconnaissance but not for travelling into enemy territory. Several miles out of Ostend a sortie came up to challenge us. Our presence must have been spotted and reported with enough time to get planes in the air and at considerable altitude. We still had the edge by at least 400 feet, but they were climbing steadily. Rogers signalled for me to return — there was no possibility of photographs that day. The Camels banked around as well, in order to engage the Hun closer to friendly territory.

I kept a close eye on the enemy's progress. Then I yelled at Tyler to man the manoeuvrable Lewis gun. He hastily stored his camera equipment and prepared to take over the gun. Somewhere close to the border of Belgium and France, eight enemy planes caught up with us.

Rogers performed a loop and the other three Camels followed. It felt strange to watch my companions head into the fray while I made every effort to leave them behind. There was no reasonable option. Once we crossed into French territory and were lower to the ground, the enemy would likely back off rather than risk the anti-aircraft guns from Dunkirk. They outnumbered us, and the Big Ack was no match for a group of Albatroses if they got past our Camels.

The chatter of machine-gun fire reached us and I took another look back. Tyler was at the ready, his gun trained at a growing black spot in the sky.

One Albatros at least had made it past our retinue and was closing in. The Big Ack was at maximum speed, about 95 miles per hour, while the Albatros could put out over 100. Tyler swivelled the Lewis gun left and right and I knew instantly that the enemy was beginning his attack. Sure enough, the bullets whined around us and the Lewis chattered its return fire behind my head.

Time was the most critical element. Too much manoeuvring slowed us down and I needed to get as close to Dunkirk, and the support of anti-aircraft fire, as possible. The Albatros pilot knew it too. I had to rely on Tyler as our best defence. I thought of poor Harry Pritchard, my last gunner, being shot to pieces long before we made it to base.

I realized that Tyler had missed his calling. In the few minutes since the chase had begun, the man transformed into a completely different animal. I had never seen a gunner so eager. Even over the noise of the engine I could hear him in snatches, screaming as he fired burst after burst.

"Come 'ere ya filthy blackbird! Take that up your tonsils! Oh, you want some more, do ya? Come to papa!" His wild banter never stopped. His safety belt had long been hurled aside. He flailed around like a madman. I kept my mouth shut, for his antics worked wonders at keeping the wolves at bay. There were two planes at us now.

Tyler suddenly screeched in triumph, and off to port I saw a plane headed down in flames.

But the second plane shot several holes in the fabric of our wing.

Tyler cursed away and opened up with a new burst of fire. A moment later a waft of smoke puffed

186

from the Big Ack's engine. The engine caught, coughed and belched a larger amount of smoke until we were completely encompassed in it.

The nose dipped. I fought with the control stick and then the flaps to keep us up. The machine gun had fallen silent so I shot a glance behind. Tyler waved at me, dutifully strapping himself back into his seat. There was a red patch growing on his shoulder, but how serious the wound was I could not tell. His grin reassured me. The Albatros had broken off pursuit and Rogers came up quickly from behind.

We still held a decent altitude, although the Channel looked alarmingly closer than it had a minute before. I could see our base at Dunkirk between the belches of smoke.

"Can we make it, sir?" Tyler yelled.

I held up my thumb. Angels help us! Could we make it?

The propeller stopped at about 400 feet and I held the Big Ack as steady as I could. The smoke was intermittent, so I used any moments of clarity to plot our landing. Men ran around on the field, preparing for us to touch down. A line of fuel trucks made their way off the track.

I estimated that we could make the first hundred yards of the base field, though we risked striking the remaining truck if we did so. But there was no option left. A ground crewman ran like the wind towards the truck. He was trying to move it before we reached him. Brave, foolish man!

The ground was close. I was dropping the nose down slowly when another billow of smoke caught me full in the face. We were too low not to complete the landing, but I couldn't see a thing. We struck hard and bounced. The wind was knocked out of me and I tried to hold the plane straight. Through the smoke I caught a glimpse of the side of the truck zooming across our nose, with the crewman ducking low to the dashboard as if he feared his head being chopped off.

My wing dipped suddenly, caught the earth and we spun around. In a split second we flipped. My head struck something and I blacked out.

Chapter 16
March 1918

I woke up in the hospital with a doctor shining a bright light in my eye.

"Hello, Lieutenant," he said casually. "Welcome back."

Once again I had sustained a concussion, and this one was a little worse than the first. I was groggy, disoriented and frequently nauseated. Headaches plagued me much of the time. I lay in bed for two days, waiting anxiously for the doctor to release me.

Rogers and Tyler filled me in on the details. The ground crew had pulled both Tyler and me out from our upside-down position.

"You did marvellously well, Stitch," Rogers commented. "The flip only happened at the end, when your speed had decreased, so the crash wasn't as bad as it could have been."

"And we got a score, sir!" Tyler said excitedly. "The bloke managed to crash-land his plane, but we got the victory. My first one, sir!"

I smiled. "You were a complete idiot up there,

Tyler. A madman." I held out my hand. "And I'd take you as my gunner any day of the week. It was an honour to fly with you."

He blushed to his roots.

Rogers coughed. "Off you go, Tyler. If you will, please. I need a moment."

Tyler shook my hand again and left. I looked up at Rogers uncertainly. "What, more bad news? Who didn't make it back?"

He shook his head. "There were no losses, Stitch. All back safe."

"Then what's wrong?"

He cleared his throat. "The doctor says you're through."

I stared. "What?"

"The war's over for you, my friend. You can marry Nellie, go home and have babies."

"I don't understand."

He put his hand on my shoulder. "You sustained two bad concussions, Paul."

"I came back after the first one, didn't I?"

He nodded. "Yes, but it took a long time for you to steady up from the first, and you've never completely healed. You've had headaches ever since. Can you imagine what you'll feel now that you've had a second? The doctor fears your symptoms may be semi-permanent. He says you're not safe to fly an aircraft. I'm sorry, lad. For many reasons, I'm sorry."

As his words slowly sunk in I felt conflicting emotions. I would be with Nellie! We could go home! But I could not fly again.

"I'm writing your papers today," Rogers continued. "You'll be on sick leave indefinitely. The doctor here believes it will lead to an honourable discharge. You're going home, old friend!"

I remained on the base for three more days while the doctor monitored my progress. Despite the hope of going home, I felt ill and off balance. Rogers wrote to my parents and to Nellie for me, as I could not stare steadily at the page, and vomited on my first attempt at writing. For the first time, I began to fear that I was indeed permanently damaged.

On March 14, 1918, I packed my kit bag, made my bed and took one last look at the inside of our hut.

"You'll make a much better home with Nellie," Rogers quipped.

A truck was waiting to get me to the docks, where a ship would take me across the Channel.

I paused at the door. "I need one more look," I said. I walked out to the field in the drizzling rain and stepped through the growing mud puddles. Five Camels sat neatly side by side, as if watching me. I could see *Hurrah!* in the middle of the pack and *Billy's Vengeance* right beside her.

"She won't be the same without you," Rogers said, coming up beside me. "But I promise you that whoever flies her will honour the memory. You're an excellent pilot, Paul. And my closest friend in this messy war. I can only be happy for you that you're getting out of it all."

I put my arm around his shoulder. "You'll visit us?"

He nodded. "England or Canada. I'll find you."

At that moment a Camel came down for a landing, a single scout, out for a brief patrol of the Channel. We watched the pilot bank around and approach the strip, his wings dipping and fighting both the feisty engine and the wind. He held her steady and brought her down, bumping and rolling along the field. As I watched, I imagined my hands on the control stick, my right foot pressed hard on the rudder. I smelled the castor oil and felt the wind on my face. It was glorious.

"Goodbye, Billy," I whispered. "Goodbye."

Epilogue

March 19, 1918

Dear Sarah,

I'm coming home! And I won't be alone either. Nellie and I will marry on the 20th of April in Redcar and then take the train to London. From there we'll board a ship to Halifax and make our way back to Winnipeg. Nellie says she knows you already through your letters and can hardly wait to see you face to face.

I can't be certain of how easy our travel will be. There is a lot of uncertainty in Europe right now. The Germans have massed enormous advances of late. There has also been more trouble with attacks against British shipping. The word on the street is that the Germans might even win the war. I can't believe it will happen — not with the likes of Rogers and Tyler chasing down the Hun in the air.

I will be most careful bringing Nellie home.

Your last letter came as a shock. I am relieved that Robert is no longer in the war. The difficult part is imagining him with only one leg. I knew the trench foot was bad, but did not realize that it had come back with such a vengeance. Poor Robert! I've actually drawn him in a picture to prepare myself for our meeting. In my mind's eye I can see him in the far pasture with the new wheat reaching as high as his knee. I've seen many men on crutches in this war, but the thought of our brother needing them for the rest of his life fairly catches my breath. We'll make it through, don't you worry, Sarah! If a man has his mind and his hands, then there is life for him on the farm.

Tell Dad not to worry about picking us up from the train station. The Lewises' farm is a short walk and I'm sure Harold will be happy to bring us home.

And one more thing: Robert isn't the only one I've drawn in the picture — you're there too, dear sister. The basket in your hands is full of seeds, all that we need to plant our own fields. One day I hope to see Rogers crossing our farm, without injury and in a time of peace. We'll shake hands and make a toast to Billy and all the others. We'll breathe the fresh air and stare into a blue sky free of bombers, bullets and fire. I'm coming home, Sarah!

Your loving brother,
Paul

* * *

Though Paul Townend's career as a flyer ended, others kept up the pressure against the German squadrons, and new aircraft and strategies continued to develop. The Sopwith Snipe, a plane created to replace the Camel, came into the war in 1918. Canadian ace William Barker flew his Sopwith Snipe alone against fifty enemy aircraft. Although greatly injured, he shot down four enemy planes before landing.

Paul's discharge also came just as a major German offensive began — so major that many people thought the Germans would win the war.

Freed up by the withdrawal of Russia from the war on the Eastern Front, they attacked quickly and with massive artillery bombardments in order to beat the Allied forces before the Americans arrived in greater numbers. A million shells were fired at the British Fifth Army. After a single day, over twenty thousand British soldiers were taken prisoner, and the Somme once again lay in German hands. However, the lightly armed storm troopers who had advanced so quickly against the British found themselves short of supplies, and unable to hold the positions they had taken.

Between March and April the Germans had lost some 230,000 men. In April 1918, the Germans also lost their number-one flying ace, the Red Baron, who was shot down behind enemy lines.

By June 1918 the Germans had pressed forward with three major offensives. After a final attack in July, the combined forces of the British, French and American armies fought back with counter-offensives in July, August and September. By October the Germans were asking for an armistice. The Kaiser abdicated the throne on November 9, and on November 11 the armistice was signed. As late as early November 1918, Allied pilots were being shot down or went missing in action.

Historical Note

Canadian pilots played an enormous role in air warfare during World War I. Many of them were farm boys who came from right across the country. Raymond Collishaw from Nanaimo, B.C., was credited with 60 victories. William Barker, credited with 50 victories, was born in Manitoba. Billy Bishop, Canada's greatest flying ace, with a record 72 victories, came from Owen Sound, Ontario. Although he only recorded 10 victories, Arthur Roy Brown of Ontario was heralded with the most successful one of all. On April 21, 1918, he was credited with shooting down Manfred von Richthofen, the Red Baron, although the actual facts of that incident are still disputed. Recent information indicates that an Australian machine-gunner on the ground may have shot the Baron after Brown's skirmish with the German ace.

Learning how to fly a plane and how to fly in combat differed for these young Canadian men. Some, like Raymond Collishaw, had to pay for their own flying lessons before heading to England and

France. In some cases the Royal Naval Air Service paid for the pilot's licence at the Curtiss Aviation School near Toronto, where pilots were trained using the Curtiss Jenny 4 (JN-4 or Canuck). Others did not receive training until they arrived in England or France. Some men had as little as 12 hours in the air before heading into the skies on their first mission.

Unlike most of their fellow British officers, the Canadian pilots did not come from well-to-do or titled families. Nonetheless, in battle and in the air, the Canadian pilots earned the respect of the British officers. Pilots came from various countries in the British Empire and squadrons were usually mixed. There were exceptions. No. 10 Squadron of the RNAS, for example, had all Canadians. Raymond Collishaw's Flight B, Black Flight — one of three flights that comprised No. 10 Squadron — consisted of five men (including Collishaw himself). These men flew in Sopwith Triplanes and named each of them to match the Black Flight theme: Collishaw's *Black Maria*, Ellis Reid's *Black Roger*, Mel Alexander's *Black Prince*, John Sharman's *Black Death* and Gerry Nash's *Black Sheep*. These men alone downed 87 German aircraft in the three months from May to July, 1917.

Aviation was a hazardous activity in the early

years of flight, even without the complications of war. On a monthly — even daily — basis throughout the war, engineers experimented with how they might make faster, more efficient planes. Ideas and inventions flourished. Before the arrival of synchronized machine guns, for example, pilots tried everything — hurling grenades, bricks, and in one case a grappling hook from the cockpit, in order to bring an enemy down. The synchronized machine gun, an invention that allowed bullets to be fired *through* a running propeller, greatly increased pilots' ability to fire straight ahead while flying.

Some inventions were successful while others resulted in disaster. At times, it was the pilots themselves who made suggestions to the engineers for improvements. It was truly a period of trial and error, with creativity spurred by the demands of war. Just when one country produced a plane with more power, an opposing nation might create an aircraft with better manoeuvrability. For example, the nimble, high-flying Gotha bombers enabled Germany to attack England at night and even in the daytime. Britain's answer was the Sopwith Camel, a machine that could not only operate well at high altitudes, but was incredibly versatile in the air.

At times, the life expectancy for new pilots at

the Western Front was abysmal: as low as 2 to 3 weeks. Crash landings, mid-air collisions and flying at night were among the hazards pilots experienced. The Sopwith Camel accounted for hundreds of non–combat-related deaths.

Dogfights could be exhilarating but extremely stressful, and pilots often required stress leave to calm their nerves and catch up on sleep. Attentiveness was crucial to survival in the air, and pilots who were exhausted or overly stressed made mistakes that endangered their own lives as well as those of their companions. Some men tried to ease their stress by drinking large amounts of alcohol; some even drank alcohol while flying.

First World War pilots firmly believed they had a better existence than the soldiers on the ground. They chose to be in control of a machine in the freedom of the open skies, despite the obvious dangers. In addition, pilots typically ate better food and slept in huts with proper bunks. They did not have to hunker down in often squalid trenches, as soldiers did at the front lines.

The public tended to see pilots as "knights of the air" — jaunty, clever, courageous and daring. Such popularity tempted some young men in their late teens and twenties to enlist. It was also not uncommon for pilots to meet their future brides when they visited French and English towns.

The purpose and usefulness of aircraft grew with every year of the war. In 1914, planes were used almost exclusively for reconnaissance — to see from the air what the enemy was doing on the ground. Enemy movements were reported back at base, and troop adjustments were made accordingly. It wasn't long before photographers went on reconnaissance flights as well. Untold thousands of aerial photos were taken.

Airplanes also took on the new role of protecting England's major cities from Zeppelin attacks. Although Zeppelins accounted for only a small amount of damage in World War I, they created a great deal of anxiety for citizens. This was especially true at night, when the giant dirigibles dropped their bombs on London and other cities. They were a terrifying spectacle, and seemingly unstoppable in the skies. Airplanes soon became a mainstay of home defence against Zeppelins for the duration of the war.

First World War flyers fought through extreme conditions, provided vital reconnaissance information, and participated in shaping the inventions and mechanisms that would change the course of warfare in the skies.

A Royal Flying Corps (RFC) plane soars above the German trenches.

Pilots needed warm jackets as well as helmets, goggles and gloves. The silk scarf many flyers wore was used to wipe engine oil from their goggles.

The Curtiss JN-4 (Jenny 4) was the plane in which many RNAS pilots did their initial training. This formation is flying above a bank of clouds.

An airman in a Curtiss JN-4 (Jenny) training machine is learning to use the machine gun.

Lt.-Colonel Raymond Collishaw (left), leader of the all-Canadian Black Flight squadron, was the first flyer to score 6 victories in one day. (Right) Lt.-Colonel William Avery "Billy" Bishop of the Royal Flying Corps was Canada's top ace. He had incredible vision and seldom wore goggles.

Pilots who were shot down could sometimes manage to land their planes relatively safely, though more serious crashes were common.

Major W. G. "Billy" Barker sits in the cockpit of a Sopwith Camel. He downed 50 enemy aircraft.

208

The huge German airships called Zeppelins (after their inventor) brought fear to the British people. This downed Zeppelin has had its outer "skin" burned away, revealing the frame inside.

PUBLIC WARNING

The public are advised to familiarise themselves with the appearance of British and German Airships and Aeroplanes, so that they may not be alarmed by British aircraft, and may take shelter if German aircraft appear. **Should hostile aircraft be seen,** take shelter **immediately** in the nearest available house, preferably in the basement, and remain there until the aircraft have left the vicinity: do not stand about in crowds **and do not touch unexploded bombs.**

In the event of HOSTILE aircraft being seen in country districts, the nearest Naval, Military or Police Authorities should, if possible, be advised immediately by Telephone of the TIME OF APPEARANCE, the DIRECTION OF FLIGHT, and whether the aircraft is an Airship or an Aeroplane.

GERMAN
AIRSHIPS

Note specially the shape of the Airships and the position of the passenger cars

BRITISH
AIRSHIPS

Note specially the sloped-back wings of the German Aeroplanes

AEROPLANES

AEROPLANES

Posters such as this helped citizens know whether a plane or airship overhead was the enemy's or their own.

210

Two Sopwith Camels engage in a dogfight with the infamous Red Baron. This illustration shows the Red Baron (centre) being chased by Canadian pilot Arthur Roy Brown.

World War 1 Aircraft

Plane	Maximum Speed	Endurance	Armament
Sopwith 11/2 Strutter	100 mph/160 kph	3.75 hours; longer with some engines	1 Lewis and 1 Vickers .303 machine guns
Sopwith Camel	113–121 mph/182–195 kph	2.5 hours	2 Vickers or 2 Lewis machine guns, or 1 of each
Sopwith Pup	99-111 mph/159-178 kph	3 hours	1 Vickers machine gun
Albatros D.III	120 mph/193 kph	2-3 hours	2 Spandau machine guns
Fokker Triplane	95-103 mph/153-166 kph	1.5 hours	2 Spandau machine guns
Gotha G.IV bomber	87.5 mph/141 kph	3.5-6 hours depending on bomb load	2-3 machine guns; racks for 14 bombs
Halberstadt D.II	90 mph/145 kph	1.5 hours	1 Spandau machine gun

Speeds varies according to altitude and engine. Estimated endurance time is for cruising speed, not combat speed.

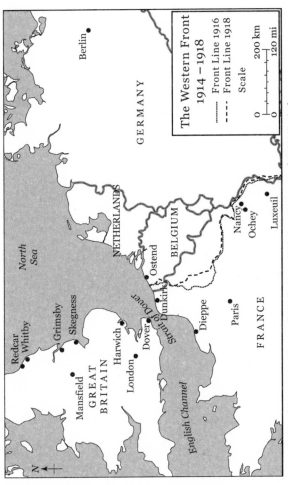

The Western Front
1914 – 1918
.... Front Line 1916
- - - - Front Line 1918
Scale
0   200 km
0   120 mi

Hundreds of Royal Air Force (RAF), Royal Flying Corps and RNAS air bases were clustered along England's east coast, and in France. The map above shows some of them.

Credits

The publisher wishes to thank Janice Weaver for her attention to the factual details, and Dr. Terry Copp for sharing his expertise. Thanks also to Steve Beth Suddaby, author of "Buzzer Nights: Zeppelin Raids on Hull," for his detailed notes on First World War aircraft.

Author's Note

World War I has always been of interest to me, ever since my mother and father first showed me my great-grandfathers' medals and military papers. My brother, Phil, built model airplanes such as the Sopwith Camel in our basement. We often talked about what it must have been like for pilots in the war. When I was in Grade Four, I wrote a research project on Charles Lindbergh. Although his flying came after World War I, it was still in the adventurous age of flight, and completely captured my interest. While researching this book, I gleaned information from pilots' journals, flight records, eyewitness accounts and military records.

As I was writing the novel, Phil helped with many, many details regarding planes and the conditions that pilots faced in the air. As a professional model builder, he learned a great deal about the details of various aircraft. His expertise was essential for this project.

The story of Paul Townend is woven from threads taken from the exploits of many of the First World

War flyers and their peers. In particular, I found accounts of Raymond Collishaw's participation in the war to be of great value. Collishaw led the famous Black Flight (officially, Flight B) — a group of five Canadian pilots. Black Flight took down 87 enemy aircraft between May and July 1917. Much of the timeline of Collishaw's service was used as my guide for Paul's duties in France from 1916 to 1918, although there are places where I have taken some liberties with the dates for the sake of the story.

Acknowledgements

Special thanks to my brother, Philip Ward, and Les Westlake, for their research and commentary; also to Stan Steiner for his encouragement in writing. The Canadian Museum of Flight in Langley, B.C., was an excellent resource and so helpful throughout the project. Also, thanks to my editor, Sandy Bogart Johnston, for her meticulous pursuit of strong writing and accuracy of information.

Other books in the
I AM CANADA series

Prisoner of Dieppe
World War II
Hugh Brewster

Blood and Iron
Building the Railway
Paul Yee

Shot at Dawn
World War I
John Wilson

Deadly Voyage
RMS Titanic
Hugh Brewster

Behind Enemy Lines
World War II
Carol Matas

A Call to Battle
The War of 1812
Gillian Chan

Storm the Fortress
The Siege of Quebec
Maxine Trottier

For more information please see the I AM CANADA
website: www.scholastic.ca/iamcanada